Preparing to
Adopt

A TRAINING PACK FOR PREPARATION GROUPS

APPLICANT'S WORKBOOK
Compiled by Shaila Shah

Published by
CoramBAAF Adoption and Fostering Academy
41 Brunswick Square
London WC1N 1AZ
www.corambaaf.org.uk

Coram Academy Limited, registered as a company limited by guarantee in England
and Wales number 9697712, part of the Coram group, charity number 312278

© BAAF, 2002, 2006, 2010, 2014
Second edition, 2006
Third edition, 2010
Fourth edition, 2014
Originally published by BAAF in 2014.
Reprinted with minor revisions in 2017 by CoramBAAF

British Library Cataloguing in Publication Data
A catalogue record for this book is available from the British Library

ISBN 978 1 910039 15 1

Project management by Shaila Shah, Director of Publications, CoramBAAF
Designed by Helen Joubert Design
Printed in Great Britain by The Lavenham Press

Contents

Acknowledgements

This edition of *Preparing to Adopt* draws on earlier editions of the course, and we would like to thank everyone who has contributed to those editions in any way over the last 12 years. It also owes a debt to the research and writing of many adoption practitioners, researchers, authors and others too numerous to mention here but whose work you will see quoted and acknowledged throughout the text.

The first edition of *Preparing to Adopt*, published in 2002, was devised by a working party from BAAF including Pat Beesley, Barbara Hutchinson, Ian Millar and Sushila de Sousa and it was written up by Eileen Fursland. A number of colleagues from BAAF assisted with preparing revised editions: Sushila de Sousa and Ian Millar contributed to the second edition published in 2006; Marjorie Morrison, Katrina Wilson, Karen Wilkins and Shaila Shah (BAAF's Director of Publications) contributed to the third edition in 2009.

The new edition of *Preparing to Adopt: Trainer's guide* has been written by Elaine Dibben, Eileen Fursland and Nicky Probert. This *Applicant's Workbook* is based on the *Trainer's Guide* and has been compiled by Shaila Shah.

Notes about the authors

Elaine Dibben

Elaine Dibben started her social work career in residential social work and qualified in 1988. She has over 20 years' experience of working in adoption and fostering in local authority and voluntary adoption agency settings and is a strong advocate for the importance of securing permanence in family settings for children who cannot return to their parents' care.

Eileen Fursland

Eileen Fursland is a freelance writer specialising in issues affecting children and young people. She has written extensively for BAAF on a number of publications, as well as for a range of magazines and national newspapers and other organisations.

Nicky Probert

Nicky Probert has been working in family placements for over 25 years and helped to set up a new adoption service where she became team manager, as well as devising preparation courses for adopters and child protection distance learning courses for foster carers.

Shaila Shah

Shaila Shah has headed up the Publications Department at BAAF for more than two decades. In her role as Director of Publications, she has commissioned and published an extensive list of titles on adoption and fostering, as well as written some information guides for children.

Welcome!

We are delighted that you are considering adopting a child.

Adoption makes a huge difference to children's lives. It will also make a big difference to your life. We hope that this Workbook and the preparation group meetings will help you understand the ups and downs, joys and sorrows, which lie ahead.

This Workbook forms part of a training pack produced by CoramBAAF for use by agencies that prepare and assess adopters, and by people who are considering becoming adopters.

Why do adopters need preparation?

Social workers are often asked: 'Why do adopters need preparation? People who have birth children are not expected to go on a training course.' This is, of course, true. So what is different about adoption?

First, the children needing adoption have had lots of experiences before coming to you.

On the whole, children who need adoptive families nowadays are not young babies whose parents have requested that they be placed for adoption. They are usually children who have had many difficult experiences and who have spent a period (or repeated periods) of time in temporary local authority care.

Although some of these children are quite young, many are of school age. They may need to be placed alongside brothers and sisters and they may need to keep in touch with members of their birth family. They may have been neglected or abused. All of this means that your experience in becoming their adoptive parent will be different from being a birth parent.

Because of this, many adoption agencies provide preparation sessions, often in groups. Such preparation helps prospective adopters find out about the extra factors involved in parenting children who have had these kinds of experiences.

The thought of being asked to join a group to learn about adoption may feel like going back to school and some people may not feel comfortable with it. But we have tried to produce a course that recognises the knowledge and skills which, by virtue of your life experiences, you already have. And we have done our best to make the course relevant to your needs.

What does preparation offer?

For anyone considering adoption, in-depth preparation is vital. It provides the opportunity to find out what adoption involves and to develop the skills that will be required as an adoptive parent. It will also help you to reflect on what adoption would mean for you.

High-quality preparation, skilfully delivered, will help you to:

- consider what adoption actually entails, for you and for a child;
- decide whether adoption is right for you and your family, and think about the kind of child/children you might adopt;
- gain a greater understanding of the needs of the children awaiting adoption;
- learn how you, as adoptive parents, could meet a child's needs;
- appreciate the nature of adoption as a lifelong process;

- identify any areas in which you need to develop in order to be approved as adopters.

This training course provides a common curriculum and a common approach to preparing adopters. And this Workbook is intended to support and expand on the material that the course leaders will present to you during the course.

Before we begin...

The present position

In 2011, the Westminster Government embarked on a major programme of adoption reform following concerns about the delays being experienced by children for whom adoption had been identified as the right plan for them to have a secure and loving family and the increasing number of these children who were then not achieving adoption.

The other related concern was the need to encourage more prospective adopters to come forward for the children waiting for adoption and to ensure they then experienced a timely response in terms of information, preparation and training to equip them for their parenting role and a quality assessment of their ability to parent children who have experienced trauma and abuse prior to their adoption placement.

In England, there is now monitoring of local authority performance in achieving timely placements for children being placed for adoption and these results are published annually through the adoption scorecard system. From 2014, there will be similar reporting on the progress of the adopter's journey. The introduction of a new two-stage assessment process that incorporates elements of preparation and training in both stages means that agencies will need to be able to offer more flexible and collaborative arrangements to enable preparation to be delivered during these shortened timescales. The two-stage process will apply to both domestic and intercountry prospective adopters.

From April 2013, there has been an equalisation of the inter-authority and inter-agency fee paid between adoption agencies for the work undertaken to prepare, assess and support prospective adopters and a legislative requirement introduced so that children and families waiting more than three months must now be referred to the Adoption Register to provide maximum opportunity for a successful match. An increased emphasis on the importance of recruiting for the national rather than local need and continuing development of Regional Adoption Agencies and consortia will mean that agencies must have confidence in the content and delivery of the preparation and training of adopters carried out by colleagues in other agencies.

Changes to adoption training and assessment

In 2012–13, the Government made a number of changes to both adoption preparation and assessment in England. The aim was to improve the adoption process. The changes came about because of concerns that some people were being deterred from adoption because of what they perceived to be a lengthy and intrusive approval process or because they believed they would not be eligible to adopt.

- The First4Adoption telephone helpline (0300 222 0022) and website (www.first4adoption.org. uk) were set up as a first port of call for anyone interested in finding out more about adoption. First4Adoption is supported and funded by the Department for Education. Advisers from First4Adoption provide general information, help prospective adopters to find adoption agencies and talk them through the options.
- The processes of application, preparation and assessment have been divided into two parts and new timescales have been introduced: two months for Stage One and four for Stage Two.
- Applicants may, if they wish, decide to take a break of up to six months between the end of Stage One and beginning Stage Two.
- The Prospective Adopter's Report (England) (BAAF, 2013) has been revised and streamlined in order to reduce the duplication of information, with a stronger emphasis on the summarising and analysis of information by the social worker undertaking the assessment.

Other Government initiatives to speed up the adoption process and encourage more people to adopt include:

- the "adoption map" of England, which shows the average waiting times for children to be adopted, by local authority area;
- adoption "scorecards", which rank local authorities in terms of the time taken to place children with adoptive families, and rank agencies for their assessment of adopters;
- the Government's "adoption passport", which sets out the support available for those who want to adopt a child. Adopters could be eligible for paid adoption leave, priority access to social housing, priority admission for school places and support services such as counselling.

This edition of *Preparing to Adopt*

Adoption preparation has changed, so this edition of *Preparing to Adopt* represents a significant change from previous editions. The course has been re-designed so that it is modular, providing more flexibility and allowing applicants to join the course at different stages. The modules have been designed to align with the two-stage adoption process.

The content of the preparation course has been updated with reference to the latest policy and guidance from the Department for Education as well as changes in practice such as "fostering for adoption" (FFA) and concurrent planning schemes. It has also been updated to reflect the complicated histories of the population of children who are currently waiting for adoptive families.

The course includes exercises involving children's profiles and case studies. Considering such profiles and case studies will help you to understand the characteristics and needs of children waiting for adoption, and help you to work out what matters to you most and what kind of child(ren) you would like to adopt.

The format of *Preparing to Adopt*

The *Preparing to Adopt* course is made up of nine separate training modules that have been broadly designed to fit within the two-stage assessment process: we envisage that agencies will use the first three of these in their Stage One training and the following six in Stage Two. However, there is no requirement about what should be covered during Stages One and Two of the assessment process so agencies may structure the modules differently to fit with their proposed model of delivering preparation and training.

Each module has been designed to be self-contained; we see all the modules as an essential part of the training course apart from *Linking, matching and introductions*, which agencies may instead choose to deliver as a post-approval module.

The modules are listed below.

- What is adoption?
- The children
- The adoption process
- Children's development and attachment
- The needs of children affected by neglect and abuse
- Becoming a parent through adoption
- Linking, matching and introductions
- Telling, contact and social networking
- Learning to live together

Depending on the time agencies decide to devote to training, this preparation course could run as separate sessions or two of the shorter sessions could be combined into a day's training. Since time for reflection is so important, it is not recommended that the modules are all run on consecutive days.

This course includes

- a trainers' guide, which contains instructions for running each training module, accompanied by a CD-ROM with PowerPoint presentations and handouts;
- a DVD with video clips;
- an Applicant's Workbook.

The Applicant's Workbook

This Workbook follows the modular structure of the preparation group programme. Each section contains useful articles, information, and worksheets to allow participants to continue to develop the themes of individual sessions. A reading list is also available from the trainer.

The Workbook will build on the content of each module by providing further information and reading and a dedicated space for you to record your thoughts and observations during the course.

The relationship between preparation and assessment

There has been a lack of clarity in the past about the relationship between preparation of adopters and the assessment process. This has been made clearer with the publication of the Government's *Action Plan for Adoption: Tackling delay* and the implementation of the two-stage process, which has been designed to offer 'initial training and preparation – clearly separated from the assessment process' (Department for Education, 2012). It is anticipated that prospective adopters will use initial preparation provided by their agency, along with online training materials being made available on the First4Adoption website and their own reading, research, learning and reflection, to develop their understanding of adoption and to consider what they have to offer before progressing to a full assessment in Stage Two.

Statutory Adoption Guidance indicates that all adopters should receive some preparation prior to their approval, which can be offered through groups or on an individual level and should take into account their existing experience and knowledge about adoption. The benefits of meeting and hearing from other adopters are also highlighted.

The content of this preparation is now set out in The Adoption Agencies (Miscellaneous Amendments) Regulations 2013 para 24 (2a–2f).It includes information about the range of children needing adoption, their likely needs and the background they may come from, the significance of adoption for a child and their family; information about post-adoption contact between a child and their birth family members, the skills needed by adoptive parents, and an understanding of the assessment process and the child's journey through care through to their placement for adoption. This information is expected to equip prospective adopters to demonstrate their understanding of what adoption will mean to them and enable them to engage with their assessing social worker during their home study.

The information that is then required for the completion of the Prospective Adopter's Report (PAR) includes an assessment of the prospective adopters' understanding of the issues involved in adoption, and their parenting capacity to meet a child's emotional and behavioural needs and support a healthy development of the child's identity through understanding their previous history and appropriate contact with their birth family. This means that there is an assumption that adopters will have had input in these areas and an opportunity to reflect on them alongside and prior to the completion of their home study assessment.

How much prior knowledge is assumed?

Applicants will join the course with widely varying levels of prior knowledge about adoption. Some will have read and researched in some depth, while others may have started exploring the subject only recently. In addition, because the course is modular, in any given session some participants may have attended one or two previous modules while others may be attending for the first time.

However, it can be assumed that everyone on the preparation course will, at the very least, have either:

- had a one-to-one conversation with a social worker about adoption;
- have attended an information session on adoption.

Don't worry if you can't remember all the information that you have been given. Discussing adoption evokes an emotional response and it is understandable if you aren't able to take everything in. In the modules that follow, you will find extracts from a wide range of titles, in which adopters share their experiences about particular aspects of adoption, be it the adoption process, parenting children affected by neglect, what becoming a parent has meant for them, learning to live together as a family, and more. Where possible, we have also included contributions from adopted children and young people, which help to see the issue from the child's point of view. Wherever possible, we have also provided information on what else you can read. When embarking on a new venture or experience, we all benefit from learning from the experiences of others who have been there and done that. It is no different in adoption. There is a wealth of narratives out there in which adopters provide candid and honest accounts of their experiences of becoming an adoptive family.

Getting the best from this course

In the past, adoption preparation has been criticised by some who say that it focuses on the difficulties and presents scenarios of "doom and gloom". The Government is keen that adoption preparation should not deter prospective adopters and that it should include the positives about adoption. Of course, sometimes everything goes well, children are delightful and bring great rewards and joy to their adopters; but it must also be acknowledged that some children present huge challenges to their adopters and everyone else around them. Adoption changes lives, and that is true for adopters as well as the children. Adopters need to be prepared for this; indeed, this is one of the purposes of adoption preparation.

Inviting experienced adopters to address the group and using some of the many online clips of positive interviews with adoptive families are good ways to accentuate the positives. Indeed, hearing about the joys of adoptive parenting first-hand from an adopter may be more powerful and authentic than hearing it from a trainer. If your trainers can arrange this, that will be very helpful. But if they can't, you can read about their experiences, as mentioned previously. After all, the aim of this preparation course is for you to find out more about adoption so that you can decide for yourself whether adoption will be right for you and your family.

The training course is designed to be dynamic and interactive. There will be group discussions, in small groups or the whole group, to help involve everybody, and get more people to open up and learn from each other. Presentations will be kept short and you will be given a copy of the PowerPoint slides and handouts. Throughout the course, you will be invited to participate in exercises – individually, in pairs or in small groups. There will be time for discussions and questions – regardless of how much knowledge you have or do not have, your ideas and contributions will be valued. You will be expected to follow certain ground rules, for example, maintaining confidentiality so that whatever you hear from other participants within the training session will not be shared with anyone else (unless it is a child protection issue, in which case it will have to be shared with the trainer, who would then take appropriate action), valuing diversity, disagreeing with an idea or viewpoint – not with the person, treating everyone with respect, and no one should express discriminatory views.

So, to get the best from this preparation course, you should:

- be committed to attending the preparation groups and participating in them;
- be prepared to spend time before each session becoming familiar with the materials provided in this Workbook;
- be prepared to give priority to any work to be undertaken between sessions;

- use the Workbook and the learning gained in the preparation groups to contribute to the home study/assessment.

Suggested reading

A list of suggested reading is included at the end of this Workbook. Reading about adoption as widely as you can is an important part of your preparation training – it will help you to learn about adoption, the range of children available, the difficulties these children may have and how you can help them, and what life as an adoptive family will be like. A number of articles and short extracts are included in the workbook itself, and you will be reading these as "homework" as part of your training course. The reading list includes details of the books that these extracts have been taken from, as well as a variety of others.

The list is divided chronologically, into books that are most suitable for each stage of your adoption journey:

- Books to read during Stage One
- Books to read during Stage Two, before panel
- Books to read while waiting to be matched with a child
- Books to read during introductions and the early days of adoption
- Books to read later on

The list will be a useful resource for you to keep referring to at different stages of your adoption journey, to ensure that your learning about adoption is a continuous, ongoing process.

Finally, don't be intimidated by the reading! We all have busy lives, and you may find it difficult to find the time to do much reading, or to manage to read entire books from the list. Simply browsing through books and reading whatever interests you, in small sections rather than the entire book, will be fine.

The decision to adopt a child is one of the most momentous anyone can make. So we all owe it to ourselves – and to the children who will go on to be adopted – to ensure that you are as well prepared as possible for what lies ahead.

MODULE 1   **What is adoption?**

Learning outcomes

This module aims to help you to:

- **understand what adoption means**
- **understand the different paths to adoption**
- **consider the qualities and capacities adopters need to have**
- **consider the child's journey to adoption**

ON ADOPTION

What is adoption?

Children whose birth family cannot provide them with a secure, stable and permanent home are entitled to have adoption considered for them.

- **Adoption is for children who cannot stay with their birth families**
- **Adoption is permanent**
- **Adopters have the same parental rights and responsibilities as other parents**
- **Adoptions today are rarely completely "closed"**

Both long-term fostering and adoption offer the child stability and security into adulthood, but in adoption the child is legally part of the adoptive family. Adoption is a legal procedure in which all parental rights and responsibilities for the child are permanently transferred by the court from the birth parents and/or the local authority to the adoptive parents. It is illegal to adopt a child without being assessed and approved by a UK adoption agency, although there are some circumstances (where a child is living with close relatives or existing foster carers) where a direct application can be made to the court.

Once an adoption order has been granted by the court (which makes the adoption legal), the adoptive parents have full legal responsibility for the child. This means they are the child's legal parents and make all decisions about the child's future. A new adoption certificate for the child is issued by the General Registrar's office and entered into the Adopted Children Register.

An **adoption order** cannot be *applied* for until a child has had a home with his or her adoptive parents, continuously, for at least ten weeks in England and Wales, and cannot be *made* by the court for 13 weeks in Northern Ireland and Scotland – although, in reality, most families have the order granted around nine to 12 months after the child moves in. Where children have already been living with their short-term foster carers or carers providing fostering for adoption placements for more than 10 weeks, their carers can make an adoption application once the placement for adoption has been formalised.

Paths to adoption

1. Adoption from care: the most common path to adoption

- Child is removed from birth parents and taken into care
- Child lives with foster carers for duration of care proceedings
- Serious search for adopters does not begin until after placement order
- When suitable adoptive parents are found, child is matched and placed with them
- When the adoption order is granted, the adoption is final

2. Fostering for adoption

- The plan for the child is adoption – local authority has discounted the possibility of return to birth family
- As soon as possible after coming into care, child is fostered by approved adopters (while waiting for formal authority to place, e.g. formal consent or placement order)
- Child continues to have contact with birth parents during court proceedings
- Fostering for Adoption carers are aware that there is no certainty of adoption till court decision or parent consents
- Child is matched with adopters if a placement order is made or formal consent is given
- Child is adopted by these adopters when legalities are finalised, if the court makes the decision that the child should be adopted and makes a placement order
- NB There are still some relinquished babies where formal consent is given after six weeks – some of these babies may be adopted via the "fostering for adoption" route

3. Concurrent planning (in baby adoptions)

- Child is removed from birth parents and taken into care
- A plan is made for assessment and rehabilitation so that child can return to birth parent(s)
- At the same time, plans are made for child to be adopted
- Child is placed with prospective adopter who is also an approved foster carer
- Concurrency carers care for the child while social workers continue to work with the birth parents
- Concurrency carers take child to birth parent(s) for regular supervised contact sessions
- If return home proves unworkable, the child is matched and then adopted by concurrency carers
  - Only used in cases where return to birth parents is considered highly unlikely
  - Concurrency carers look after the child with a view to adopting the child but at the same time they understand that rehabilitation is also being explored and that there is a possibility the child will return home. Concurrency carers are required to balance their own wishes and desires with an acceptance of what is deemed to be best for the child.

The child's journey to adoption

Figure 1 Routes by which a child becomes looked after and potentially is placed for adoption

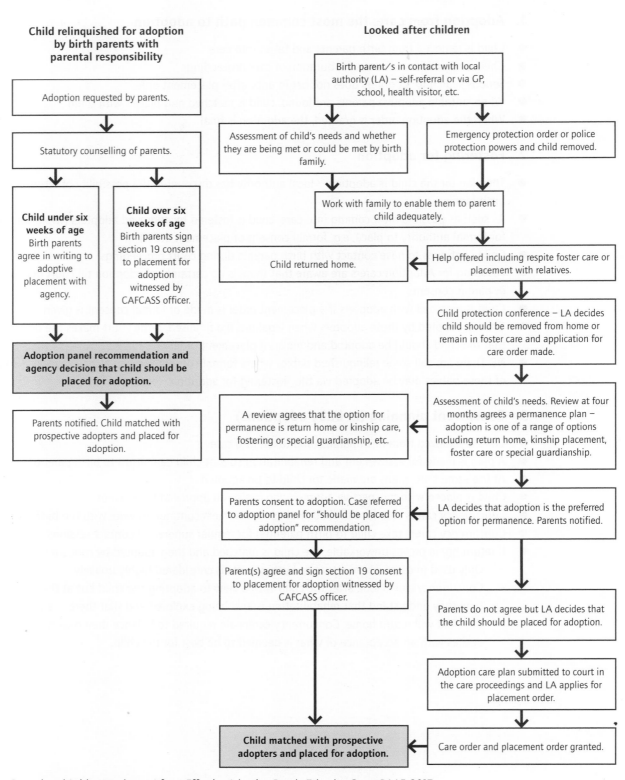

Reproduced (with amendments) from *Effective Adoption Panels*, 7th edn., CoramBAAF, 2017.

Figure 2 **The Adoption Planning Process in England and Wales**

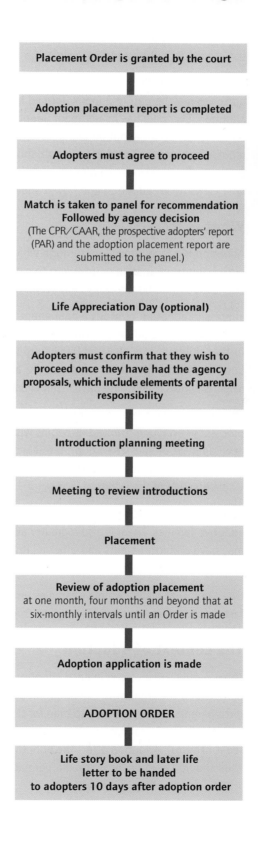

Placement Order is granted by the court

Adoption placement report is completed

Adopters must agree to proceed

Match is taken to panel for recommendation
Followed by agency decision
(The CPR/CAAR, the prospective adopters' report
(PAR) and the adoption placement report are
submitted to the panel.)

Life Appreciation Day (optional)

Adopters must confirm that they wish to
proceed once they have had the agency
proposals, which include elements of parental
responsibility

Introduction planning meeting

Meeting to review introductions

Placement

Review of adoption placement
at one month, four months and beyond that at
six-monthly intervals until an Order is made

Adoption application is made

ADOPTION ORDER

Life story book and later life
letter to be handed
to adopters 10 days after adoption order

Adoption – a brief history

Adoption is about providing a family for children whose birth parents cannot care for them. It transcends all cultures and has existed for centuries.

Adoption personally touches many people. Many of us know someone who is adopted; we ourselves may be part of a family formed by adoption or have lost a family member through adoption. Everyone has heard about adoption: as well as news items about adoption, stories of babies given up for adoption and parents and children being reunited after many years are a regular feature in soap operas and talk shows. People often feel passionately about it. Adoption policy is often controversial and sometimes has to change in response to the public's strongly held views about adoption and how it should operate.

What is it?

Adoption is a legal procedure through which a permanent family is created for a child whose birth parents are unable or unwilling to care for the child or are legally prohibited from doing so. The focus should be the child's long-term welfare.

Successful adoption provides a permanent home which is secure and meets the individual child's needs. At its best, adoption also meets the needs of the adoptive family who wanted a child or further children, as well as the family into which the child was born, who have willingly or unwillingly surrendered the child. Legally, adoptive parents have the same rights and responsibilities they would have if the child had been born to them.

Though the legal event of adoption occurs on a particular day, adoption is actually a long process for everyone involved. It begins with identifying and assessing the child who needs a new family. It progresses through the search for a suitable adoptive family who can meet the needs of that particular child. It continues through the legal procedures, and on through the whole lifespan of the adoptive family.

Researchers have increasingly been identifying the particular strengths and difficulties of adoptive families. There is also a greater awareness of the effect that long-term grief and loss may have on birth parents and other relatives of the child. This has affected the way adoption practice has developed.

One thing that makes adoptive families unique is the role of the child's biological heritage – the fact that two families are forever linked through the child.

The context of adoption

Three parties are involved in each adoption – the birth parent or parents, the adoptive parent or parents and the child, with the adoption agency acting as intermediary. Ideally, adoption offers birth parents the opportunity to plan for the care of their child when his or her need for a permanent family cannot be met in any other way (though of course some birth parents may not see it like this). Adoption offers the adoptive parents the satisfactions of parenting a child. The child should hopefully be assured a permanent home with a family able to provide appropriate care while recognising his or her origins. The rights of each party must be protected by good adoption practice as well as through legal safeguards.

Extended families are also involved in the adoption. Adoption workers are increasingly recognising the contribution of the wider family network as they learn more about cultural groups in which the extended family plays an important role. Part of good adoption practice lies in involving these family members in the adoption process.

Western European, American and a number of other cultures believe that the family is the best place for a child to grow. Adoption mirrors the social changes taking place in the society in which it is practised. It is changing all the time, as society changes and as the needs of children, birth parents and prospective adoptive parents change.

A brief history of adoption

The beginnings

Do you remember the Bible story about the baby in the bulrushes? The baby Moses was left in a basket among the reeds by his mother, who hid and watched as the Pharaoh's daughter found the baby and took him in. That was the first recorded adoption.

The history of adoption in the United States and Great Britain is interwoven, because our two countries share a common language and legal traditions. Looking at the history of adoption in the Western tradition, there have been five distinct periods, each one reflecting the preoccupations of the time.

The first period

In Greek and Roman times, most adoptions were carried out to serve the interests of the adoptive parents rather than the child. Adoptions of related young males were arranged in order that a family might not die out, or even to cement political alliances between powerful families.

In ancient Greece, the earliest known law regulating adoption dates from 594 BC and includes reference to inheritance.

Under Roman law, the adopted child could not be deprived of his rights, even if legitimate children were subsequently born to the family. The adopted sons of Roman emperors even inherited their father's empire.

The second period

In more recent times, the second stage in the evolution of adoption begins with the idea of providing some security for orphaned and "illegitimate" children. In both Great Britain and the United States in the 19th century, there was a tradition of care for such children in institutions such as workhouses during the children's early years. Children were then "indentured" to families, which means they were taken in, fed and clothed, educated and taught a trade in return for their work on behalf of the family.

However, by the mid-19th century, in the United States and in Britain, both the indenture system and the workhouses were becoming overwhelmed by the numbers of destitute children needing care and education. There were demands for better care for children. These demands coincided with the religious revivalism of the second part of the 19th century. A number of different denominational groups and individual philanthropists, such as Dr Barnardo, opened big orphanages and institutions for the care of children. However, these institutions had serious problems with infant mortality and, increasingly, attempts were made to place children with families.

At about the same time, there was a movement in both the American west and in Scotland to board out children from urban regions into family foster homes in rural areas. The agricultural homes of the American west could use the labour of large families and placements were free, whilst Scottish crofters welcomed the small allowance paid, which helped to supplement their meagre incomes. These foster homes were regarded as substitutes for the birth family and sometimes a situation similar to an adoption evolved. "Adopted" children were expected to work hard, behave well and be grateful to the adopters.

Legal provision for adoption was made in the middle of the 19th century in most of the United States, but in England the first adoption law was not passed until 1926. The main reasons for this delay were:

- the stigma attached to births outside marriage and fears that adopted children might inherit traits, including "immorality" and "bad habits" – an attitude that, until about 1945, limited adoption mainly to the working class;
- the British courts' close guarding of the rights of parents;
- the reluctance to see inheritance passed on to "outsiders";
- the social class system, and the maintenance of class lines based on kinship.

The problems of increased "illegitimacy" and the huge numbers of children orphaned as a result of World War I, along with many custody disputes over "adopted" children, meant that adoption in England finally had to be regulated by law: this was the 1926 Adoption Act.

The adoption order, once made, was irrevocable. This first British adoption law preserved the adopted child's right to inherit from the natural family, but specified that the adoptive family must make specific provision if the child was to inherit from them.

During the period between the two world wars, a number of societies were set up to arrange adoptions.

In the United States, in the years between the two world wars, infant adoptions began to gain in popularity. Major factors were the drop in the birth rate that followed World War I and the influenza epidemic of 1918, the development of formula milk for babies, which made infant adoption possible, and the growing perception that environment was as important as heredity in shaping a child's personality. By 1929, all states had adoption legislation. These laws continued to focus on the welfare of the child.

Between 1923 and 1933 increasing numbers of regulations were written, requiring investigations of prospective adoptive homes and trial periods in adoptive homes. Provision that records of adoptions be sealed and that a new birth certificate be issued for the child were designed to protect the child from the stigma of illegitimacy, as well as to make sure that the adoptive family was protected from "interference" by the birth family.

The third period

The period following World War II marks a third stage, during which adoption was viewed as a solution to the problem of infertility and became popular among the middle classes of both Britain and the United States. This came to be known as the era of the "perfect baby" for the "perfect couple". Great effort was put into matching infant and parents, in an attempt to create a family as "like" a biological one as possible. An "adoptable" infant was, generally speaking, white, healthy, with an acceptable background and developing normally.

Adoptive couples were subjected to intensive investigations in order to assess their capacity as parents. As the number of applicants began to exceed the number of babies available, the definition of the "perfect" couple became increasingly restrictive, with narrow limits of age, the length of marriage and residence in a community, and demands for comfortable income and housing. Generally, the religion of the adopting family had to match that of the infant.

By the late 1960s, almost three-quarters of the children adopted by non-relatives in Britain and in the United States were under one year old. Those who were older or who had even a minor disability were not even considered and were likely to be raised in residential nurseries. The characteristic feature of this period was a "child for a home", which meant that there was more interest in the needs of adopting parents rather than in the interests of the children.

During this time of infant adoptions, it was assumed that, after the legal completion of the adoption, the family was "just like any other family". It was not expected that any further services would be needed. Follow-up studies (though they had limitations) indicated that the children in these adoptive homes did well and that parents were satisfied. The cost to the community was minimal. Adoption gained popularity and respectability.

The fourth period

This period is associated with a decisive shift towards a more child-centred adoption practice. From about the mid-1960s onward in the United States and early 1970s in Britain, there has been a drastic drop in the number of young white children available for adoption. This is partly because of more effective contraception and the legalisation of abortion. It is also the result of society's increasing acceptance of single parenthood and the provision of state welfare benefits to support single parents.

As fewer babies were released for adoption, many adoption agencies, overwhelmed with large numbers of adoptive applicants, closed their waiting lists to those seeking a healthy white baby. Many adoption societies which had concentrated on placing healthy white babies closed and their records were transferred to social services departments.

Social services and the remaining voluntary agencies then began to be less rigid about which children were "adoptable" and who could adopt.

During the 1960s and 1970s, studies revealed that in Britain and the United States there were thousands of children who were in institutions or in unstable fostering arrangements without realistic prospects of returning to their own families. These were not the children traditionally seen as suitable for adoption, but older children, sometimes with mental or physical disabilities, children of mixed race, or groups of siblings. Many of the children came from backgrounds of abuse and neglect. The children's birth families had in most cases either disappeared, felt the system discouraged them from maintaining links, or were unable to make a home for them but were unwilling to relinquish them for adoption. There was mounting pressure for agencies to plan for these "special needs" or "hard to place" children. Moving children from the care system into adoptive homes proved also an attractive option to social services departments who otherwise faced many years of funding residential or foster care placements.

In both Britain and the United States, numerous projects showed that, with imaginative recruitment methods, adoptive homes could be found for these waiting children, and that these adoptions could work. The search now was for "a home for a child", moving adoption towards a much more child-centred approach. This shift was greatly helped by studies showing that adoptions of older children could work well.

As agencies have had success, children with increasingly severe disabilities and emotional difficulties have been placed for adoption, and adoptive homes have been found for adolescents and sibling groups.

Now other families were considered suitable to adopt: families from a variety of class and economic backgrounds, those who had experienced divorce, single parents, foster parents, older parents and those with children. The special needs of some of the children needing homes stretched the economic capacity of many families who would otherwise adopt, and some families who were interested in "hard to place" children did not have the resources to add a child to the family. To facilitate these adoptions, a system of adoption subsidies, or adoption allowances, from public money developed first in the United States, and then in Great Britain. Forced to focus on the qualities that really mattered in parenting difficult children successfully, adoption agencies dropped their arbitrary requirements.

The fifth period

Now it looks as though a fifth period may be emerging in the development of adoption. This is evident, for example, in some aspects of intercountry adoption and in recent attempts to deregulate adoption in Britain in order to allow "market forces" to play a greater role, as in the United States.

There has been an emphasis in recent British legislation and in the "family preservation" movement in the United States on the rehabilitation of birth families. Some of the provisions of the Children Act 1989 can lead to unacceptable delays in providing some children with new families.

In the US, independent adoptions in which a lawyer or doctor acts as intermediary, or in which birth parents and adoptive parents reach an agreement on their own, are legal in all but six states and have become increasingly important as a source of white infants. Such arrangements are illegal in Britain. Some fear that, in the USA at least, the emphasis on adoption may be once again shifting towards the rights of adults, rather than on the needs and rights of children who need families.

Adapted with permission from *Adoption: Theory, policy and practice*, Cassell, 1997 © John Triseliotis, Joan Shireman and Marion Hundleby

ON PREPARATION COURSES

Our first adoption workshops

I've never really relished "Induction" days whenever I've started a new job. The "Introductions" in particular terrify me – standing up, apprehensive, red-faced, struggling to describe my finer points for the delight of a captive audience.

I wonder what I might say about myself, if asked, at our first adoption workshop. I imagine I would say that I'm gregarious, caring, a good friend, an avid reader, a dog lover, knowledgeable about wine, an aspiring novelist and a dreadful cook.

If asked about my husband, I would say that he is witty, dependable, a good listener, a Mini (car) fanatic, hideously untidy, brilliant with computers – and my very best friend.

So I start to wonder, as the day of reckoning beckons, will we actually have to stand and announce ourselves or will I be able to remain anonymous – a vigilant observer, quietly blending into the background?

Saturday 11 May 2002

When it comes, the morning could not have had a more disastrous start. Just as we are about to head for the train station, en-route to London, we have an electrical fire in the hallway. Clearly not wanting to leave an unsafe house, we have to leave a message for our adoption agency and hastily call out an electrician.

This does nothing to help our nerves. It is the first day of our adoption workshop and all is not well!

Ringing our agency once more, I explain that with two train connections to catch, we will be with them by 11am. The course is due to start at 9.45am. We will be at an instant disadvantage and will feel decidedly uncomfortable walking in on a room full of people, probably all staring at us. What a great start to the day. We assure each other that the reality cannot be that bad.

But it is.

It is awful.

Sixteen people, all wearing name badges, sitting in a grim-faced circle. If it hadn't been for the amiable social worker, trying to make us feel welcome, I think we'd have walked out then and there. I console myself that at least we have missed the introductions.

Everyone breaks for coffee after we arrive, so this gives the social worker time to fill us in on what we have missed. Then our name badges and folder of notes are handed to us, and we take our seats in the circle. I immediately feel sick with nerves.

The first exercise after the break is "ripping paper". It is powerful stuff and a very clever way of bringing home the upheaval that most adopted children have suffered in their short lives. The social worker, Dee, takes a large sheet of paper and asks us all to contribute experiences and factors that make us the person we are today. She writes down: home, parents, school, friends, pets, hobbies, travel, stability, family, guidance, discipline, neighbours, clubs, holidays. These are just a few of the suggestions put forward. Dee then takes the large sheet of paper and rips it into shreds, symbolic of the fragmented life of the adopted child.

Quite thought-provoking really, like literally having the rug pulled from beneath your feet. Every facet of the child's life, any pattern of continuity just torn to pieces as the child is moved time and time again – saying goodbye to parents, siblings, carers, peers and a house they probably thought was their home.

Dee then scatters the torn pieces of paper onto the floor in a complete jumble; a few pieces flutter away and are lost altogether. She demonstrates just how difficult it is to try and put the bits back together again, like a jigsaw with missing pieces. Most of them just do not seem to fit and it would take masses of patience and time to fit them together again properly.

In much the same way as an adopted child would probably come to us with his or her entire history scattered in tiny pieces.

The next exercise is equally powerful and beautifully simple. A second social worker shows us a bag containing a few treasured possessions, which a six-year-old may have accumulated over the years – maybe it's a faded scarf or a Christmas card from a foster carer, an old train ticket, a broken toy, or something that reminds them of a sister or brother. There is no need for words. The exercise serves to reinforce what should have been obvious to us: that all of the child's belongings should be kept in a special, safe place, not washed and tidied away, and that children should be encouraged to talk about the contents of their treasure bag or box whenever they want to.

It is a very moving exercise and many people begin to look visibly upset.

It is surprising to see that there isn't a broader cross-section of people on our course. We expected more single applicants, more council tenants and not just "homeowners". They pretty much all live in London apart from Rob and me – and quite a few of them already have children, which is another surprise to us. A lot of them are quite a bit older than we are – perhaps a factor in how solvent they appear to be, which one couple seems at pains to emphasise. They point out that, although they have a huge house, their own businesses and lots of money, they still feel excluded from their neighbours' gatherings because they don't have children. It is as if money can buy them everything else in life and yet they still don't fit in – so enter the adopted child to help ease matters at their next summer barbecue.

It is astounding to hear this particular couple's motivation for adoption. Nearly everyone else on our course seems very pleasant and as nervous as we are. It is just not quite what we'd been expecting.

On a more positive note, however, it is encouraging to see three couples of mixed ethnicity and an Asian couple on our course, as it is common knowledge that there are not enough black or mixed ethnicity adopters coming forward. Often black children and children of dual heritage end up staying in care for a very long time, so it is great to see that we are not all white.

Group work comes next. It is one of the things that I've been dreading most – often lacking in confidence in such situations. It just shows how wrong you can be. This first group-work exercise, in fact, is a turning point for us all – enabling everyone to interact with one another and certainly helping us all to relax a bit more.

From *An Adoption Diary*, by Maria James, published by BAAF in 2006 (pp 12–15). This personal narrative follows Maria and Rob, her husband, as they go through the adoption process. © Maria James

If you can't hack a course like this one...

Our "preparation" is a shared experience and we are part of a group of 17 attending this course, packed into a room only just about big enough to squeeze us all in. Then there are the three social workers: Lesley and Debra who are running the course and one more, our old friend Penny, rather ominously there to observe and make notes.

We have joined the group to learn, but it is made clear that we will be subject to scrutiny throughout the four days. Certainly everything about the sessions has been set up to make them open and non-threatening, but the presence of an observer is a little unnerving and I wonder to what extent that is affecting or inhibiting the group's behaviour. So far, I think I've done an OK job of keeping my natural irreverence and fondness for inappropriate *non-sequiturs* in check, but goodness knows if I can keep it up for four days.

Still, it's been great to meet so many people going through the same process we are, and all having arrived at the same point. We are a mixed bunch, so it has been enlightening to talk to the others about how they reached this stage and why they have decided, as we have, that adoption is for them. Some of the group have been down the IVF road like Lesley and me, while others already have birth children and have chosen adoption to build their families further. Gluttons for punishment, I can't help thinking, but there you are, and talking with them helps us to understand their personal motivations.

One of these couples already has considerable experience as foster carers and they have brought a quite different slant to the discussions, along with bags of knowledge that the rest of us feel the need to catch up with.

Before we started the Preparation Group yesterday, the whole notion of training to be adopters seemed an odd one. Many of our friends have been shocked and even outraged when they found out that we have to do this – offended on our behalf that anyone could dare suggest it might be necessary.Two days in, and I would say that it is. Whether we will actually learn much during the course I don't know, but the Preparation Group is much more than that. It's about arranging all those jumbled thoughts you might have about adoption into the right order. It's about seeing the world from the child's perspective. And it's about testing yourself.

If you can't hack a four-day course like this one, then you might as well pack up and go home. Or at least re-evaluate where you really are. Adoption is a lifelong commitment and, after these last couple of days, Lesley and I are more certain than ever that we are in it for the long haul.

Taken from *Frozen*, by Mike Butcher, published by BAAF in 2010 (pp 179–180). This personal narrative follows Mike and his wife Lesley through IVF treatment that proves to be dangerous, before they decide to apply to adopt. © Mike and Lesley Butcher

Just the beginning...

The first day was spent looking at what adoption actually means. The real revelation to us was the fact that even if we adopted a very young baby, he or she could bring with them a serious amount of physical and emotional baggage. The second day we had to change rooms, so asked at the reception for the Carlton Suite. In a booming voice, the woman behind the counter said: 'Oh, for adoption?' I raised my eyebrows to David and we walked on. Why should she be discreet about it? Because it's private. Adoption lives in that strange no-man's land. Our business. And yet half the world – from the police to doctors and social workers, and friends who have to be your referees – has to know about it. But we need to stay in control of the information. Ultimately it belongs to us and to our child. That day we went into some rather harrowing details of the kinds of abuse adopted children might have suffered. Not just the headline-grabbing sexual abuse and physical violence, but also the subtle, often long-term effects of early neglect, of lack of stimulation and attention, which may manifest themselves fully only when a child goes through the school gates years later.

When we returned the following week, we learnt about child development and attachment patterns. We needed to remember that these children simply behave like, well, children. But sometimes adopted children have particular problems that require special attention: tantrums among older children and serious attachment difficulties for children who have been in and out of different homes for years.

The final session began with a look at the everyday challenges for adopters and moved on to look at what to do about telling your child the story of his or her life. When and how can we tell them they've been physically abused as babies? When should we inform them that they have a "tummy mummy" as well as their "forever mummy"? And how on earth would you even start to explain some of the horrific histories of daddy killing mummy, or child rape? Children's Services wanted us to be aware of all the possible scenarios; a particular child may be affected by many, a few, or none of them.

As we left, we were told that this was just the beginning and we had now to make the big decision about whether to continue on this journey. We'd learnt about what could happen when adopting a vulnerable child. But we'd also listened to real adopters and seen them glow with pride at the progress of their children: real children, their children, in thriving families. And we heard about all the daily challenges they bring: slippers flushed down toilets; problems with school work and slow development; tantrums and the refusal to eat the food they have in front of them. As my friend and mother of two boys pointed out, this sounds like being a parent.

The day we finished the course we took the puppy for a walk and then cooked ourselves a special meal, so that we could sit outside and talk over the whole process. We'd had a mini-interview that afternoon, just to review our impressions and ask any last-minute questions. We'd had none. The course had been a very positive experience and we were ready to go. We'd filled in the application by Sunday night, walked to the post-box together and, together, put the envelope into the box. Fingers crossed. For what, we didn't know. But we felt strangely elated.

Within two weeks, we received a letter informing us that our application had been accepted and that we would be allocated a link worker shortly. And sure enough, our link worker, Anna, entered our lives six weeks after the preparation course, to become our closest confidante for the months ahead.

Taken from *Take Two*, by Laurel Ashton, published by BAAF in 2008 (pp 55–57). This personal narrative follows Lesley and her husband David through IVF and various alternative therapies in their attempts to have a child, before charting their adoption of two baby girls. © Laurel Ashton

Adoption

A *family gets together*
Days are good
Only just got to know them
Put some candles on a cake
Think I'm going to like it here
I *can be happy*
Only 1 day to go
Nobody knows how good it feels

This poem, by Emily, aged 7, is taken from *I Wish I had been Born From You*, by Karen Lomas, published by BAAF in 2009 (p 9). This collection of writings, poetry and artwork by herself and her adopted daughter follows Karen's journey to adoption and her feelings about adoptive motherhood. © Karen Lomas

What I have to offer/what I can bring to adoption

....

....

....

....

....

....

....

....

....

....

....

....

....

....

....

....

....

....

....

....

....

....

....

MODULE 2: **The children**

Learning outcomes

This module aims to:
- **explain why some children need to be adopted**
- **give you a better understanding of the kind of children who are waiting and their varied backgrounds**
- **explain how you can find out about children waiting to be adopted**

ON THE CHILDREN NEEDING ADOPTION

Who are the children who need adoption?

Are there any babies needing adoption?

Of the 4,690 looked after children adopted in England in the year to March 2016, just 230 were babies under one. Proportionate figures for Scotland are similar. Today it is easier for women to choose to parent on their own and fewer single mothers are placing their babies for adoption. Contraception is more efficient than it used to be, and fewer unplanned pregnancies occur. It is also easier to terminate pregnancies than previously.

There are more white people interested in adopting a white baby without disabilities than there are such babies needing adoption. Agencies have little difficulty in finding suitable adopters for white babies without disabilities. This means that people who want to adopt only such a child are likely to find it hard even to get started on the adoption process and may not be able to adopt a baby. However, agencies are somewhat less successful at finding black families or those from other minority ethnic groups, although they are getting better at it. This means that if you and /or your partner are black or from a minority ethnic group, you are more likely to find an agency to take up your application quite quickly. You will probably have a shorter wait before being linked with a baby, although this will vary as only quite small numbers of black babies and those from other minority ethnic groups are placed for adoption each year. If you can consider slightly older children, your wait could be shorter.

There are babies with disabilities or disabling conditions such as cerebral palsy and Foetal Alcohol Spectrum Disorder who need to be adopted. There are also some babies with genetic factors in their background, such as schizophrenia or Huntington's Chorea, for whom it is not always easy to find adoptive families.

Toddlers and pre-school children

Children aged between one and five are the largest group of children adopted in the UK. This reflects the wishes of many adopters to parent pre-school children and the relative ease with which adoption agencies are able to recruit adopters for young children. The majority of these placements work out extremely successfully. However, these children often have complex needs. They may have been abused and neglected and given little opportunity to make attachments to reliable parent figures. They may be very confused about all that has happened in their short lives and be unable to trust in anyone. In addition, there may also be uncertainties about their development, which may not be resolved until they are older. Families need to be able to take on these issues and to access support and advice.

What about older children?

Many children waiting to be adopted are aged five or over. They may have lived for some years with one or both of their parents, or other family members, or they may have had many moves in and out of foster homes, and the damage done by these experiences can last a very long time. Older children need especially resilient parents who can help them face up to the past – including their possible need to keep in touch with some members of their family – and see them through the difficult adolescent years to maturity. In a loving and secure home, most of these children will eventually begin to thrive, although the older they are, the longer it may take.

Children who have been looked after by a local authority for months or years are likely to have emotional and behavioural problems because of the experiences which led to them having to be separated from their birth families, but also because of not having a permanent parent figure in their lives. Even young children soon learn that there isn't much point in getting attached to an adult who is soon going to disappear out of their lives. They may find it difficult to become attached to a new family and are likely to test out their new parents with challenging behaviour. Young children may be more like babies in their behaviour sometimes, and even teenagers may act like very young children. But most children of all ages can eventually settle when they realise that they really are part of the family.

There are children who have been so hurt by their past experiences that they will go on having special needs throughout their childhood, even though they have clearly benefited from becoming a loved member of the family. If you adopt a child who is likely to have particular ongoing needs, you should ensure as far as possible that the agency will make arrangements for them to have any special help they may continue to require on a long-term basis.

On a bad day I see the damage and wonder how I'll ever give enough, how I'll ever make enough of an impact to compete and triumph over the impact of the abuse that has robbed my daughter of years of her life and has the potential to rob her of her whole life...On a good day I know I am winning and feel I am the luckiest mother in the world.

Adoptive mother, *Adoption Today*

Groups of brothers and sisters

About half of all the children waiting for adoptive families are in groups of brothers and sisters needing to be placed together. Most of these children are in groups of two, although there are some groups of three or more. Brothers and sisters can provide support and comfort for each other throughout their lives. If they want to stay together and if an assessment of their needs has shown that one family could parent them successfully, it is very sad if they have to be separated because no families come forward for them all. You may be daunted by the practicalities, but extra help and support could and should be available (see Chapter 5). Brothers and sisters share a family history and can support each other in making sense of what has happened to them. Research indicates that, compared to children of the same age placed on their own, brothers and sisters placed together are likely to do as well or better.

There can be rivalry and spats, and their perception sometimes is that they "hate" each other! But it's obvious that having each other is a tremendous reassurance. It is the only constant and stable thing they've had in their lives.

Adoptive parents of three brothers, *Be My Parent*

Disabled children

Disabled children may be placed for adoption at a very young age when their parents feel unable to care for them, or they may be looked after by the local authority after their parents have tried unsuccessfully to cope. So they may feel the impact both of their disability, the loss of their family of origin, and perhaps the confusion of a residential setting where different staff come and go. People who adopt these children will need to be prepared for a challenging yet rewarding task, as some of the children will never be able to lead entirely independent lives. In some cases, experience of disability in prospective adopters – either their own personal or professional experience or that of their children – will be positively welcomed.

The other thing about adopting older children is that you know if there are any medical issues or developmental issues. A lot of the issues that affect children in care will be evident, whereas if they are a year old, you might not know.

Adoptive parent, *The Pink Guide to Adoption*

Learning disabilities/difficulties

There are many babies and older children who have learning difficulties/disabilities waiting for adoption, for example, children with Foetal Alcohol Spectrum Disorder. These are children who, as well as individual love and care, need additional help and support to enable them to participate in as many as possible of the experiences and opportunities open to any other child.

There are many children whose learning disabilities are not clear-cut: they may have suffered an accident or injury while very young which has affected their ability to learn or to understand the world around them – but no one knows how much. Or they may have been born with a disability that isn't clear to doctors. They may have been chronically neglected and/or abused as a baby and young child, and the extent of the damage this has caused and the possibility of change may still be unclear.

Our fourth birth child taught us not to be afraid of disability. She was born with Edward's Syndrome, and through this we became aware of the disabled children left in hospital because their parents found it too difficult to cope. So we decided to adopt.

Adoptive mother of two disabled children, *Could you be my Parent?*

Physical disabilities

There are many types of physical disability – cerebral palsy, muscular dystrophy, spina bifida and cystic fibrosis are just some of them. Children with these disabilities need the love and security that life in a family offers just as much as other children do. And, like most children, they will give love and affection in return. Having a physical disability does not mean having a learning disability too, although people sometimes confuse the two. People with physical disabilities can lead increasingly independent lives nowadays – especially if they have the support of a loving family.

Are children from different ethnic backgrounds waiting to be adopted?

Yes, there are children from a great variety of ethnic, cultural and religious backgrounds waiting for adoption. They all need families who will cherish and value their heritage and identity; families who either match their ethnicity, culture, religion and language as closely as possible, or who can actively promote these aspects of their identity.

Reproduced from *Adopting a Child*, the definitive guide to adoption, by Jenifer Lord, published by CoramBAAF in 2016 (pp 8–14). © CoramBAAF

I survived with the help of a playpen...

Our adopted children Hamish, Sophie and Emily, are full siblings. They have two more brothers, who also live with adoptive families, and we meet with one of them regularly. All three of our children were premature (31, 24 and 34 weeks), though, according to birth mum, that is genetic and runs in her family. However, it is widely known that excessive drinking during pregnancy is harmful and can result in pre-term delivery and decreased birth weight.

All our children had a very low birth weight: Hamish weighed 1,800gms and was considered small even for his premature delivery. He stayed one month in special care. Sophie weighed merely 720gms and spent almost 17 weeks in hospital. There had been only a 50:50 chance that she would live. Even after she was in foster care, she stopped breathing several times. Emily was the "biggest" and weighed 2.21kg; she had also had the longest gestation at 34 weeks. All children had been removed at birth and gone into foster care. However, there was some contact with birth mum and dad, if and when they attended.

Hamish spent 20 months in foster care and had had three foster placements and one stay in a mother and baby unit before he came to us. Multiple placements can lead to attachment problems and a sense of not belonging, as early bonding is disrupted by frequent changes of the carer.

The girls were "luckier" and had only been with one foster carer. The first time we set eyes on Hamish and Sophie, we were amazed by how tiny Sophie was. Until she was about seven years old she was always smaller than her peers. When she started walking, people were amazed to see such a tiny child on her feet so early. Hamish was a bit of a bruiser and grew to be larger than average. Sadly, this didn't do him any favours, as everybody mistook him for an older child and expected more of him. Already when we first met him, we noticed that he was very unsteady on his legs and yet it took another year to have him diagnosed with Hemiplegia (a partial paralysis affecting one side of the body). When he came to us, he did not know how to play and had very limited speech. Our concerns were ignored or dismissed as he was "just lazy" or a "typical boy", slow to learn. We eventually managed to get him speech therapy, which paid off: it is now hard to get a word in! He was a very happy child but used to dribble at an awful rate. He was also very late potty training and we still have issues with bedwetting and soiling today, which apparently is not uncommon in children with FAS.

The first few weeks seemed to go by in a flash and it was exhausting looking after two such young children. Hamish had not been taught to feed himself and Sophie had not been put on solids, so there I was, with one each side of me, handing a spoonful to each in turn. Luckily Hamish was a good eater. Sophie was fussier and stayed on her bottles for a very long time. As she was so tiny she had to have lots of additional supplements and special injections for her respiratory system.

I survived with the help of a playpen, in which I could put one child while I was attending to the other's needs, especially when Sophie was having one of her full-blown tantrums.

Reproduced from an account by Sally Baker of adopting siblings with Foetal Alcohol Syndrome (FAS), which appeared in *Parenting a Child Affected by Parental Substance Misuse*, by Donald Forrester, published by BAAF in 2012 (pp 56–58). © Sally Baker

So what do we know about Tom?

So then, what do we know about the background of the little boy who was to become our son? Who, forgive me for being so blunt, could have been any old Tom, Dick or Harry. For though if asked outright, if probed on the subject, we will admit we do believe we were somehow always meant to be a family, so perfect is our match, the fact remains he simply was not always ours. Once upon a time he belonged to someone else. And that is a difficult story to have to tell him – perhaps an unwelcome intrusion into his healthy, rock solid sense of self and his sense of belonging. Difficult for both of our children for whom it will always remain something of a Brothers Grimm fairy tale. Though there is nothing fictitious about Tom.

If you were to meet Tom he'd introduce himself. The first thing you would notice is his silly grin, his baby soft curls and his dancing green eyes. Tom is one of life's winners; though only a toddler, you can see it straightaway. He draws others in and appears to charm effortlessly. Make no mistake, he is a rogue through and through and the rages he flies into are something else altogether; at times he manages to shock even himself. We attribute this to his strawberry blonde roots that glimmer with more than just the merest hint of red. Naturally, it should go without saying but I'll get it in anyway, the charismatic, charming, cute bits of Tom come from us. Not for the first or last time in our family does the infamous nature versus nurture debate raise its head.

* * *

The information we have about Tom's birth family comes from Sarah and her mother, Tom's maternal grandmother. Sarah never took him home from hospital and it was six months later, after Tom's social worker, Jo, bound by procedure and protocol, had worked tirelessly to find him the right family as quickly as was possible, that we brought him home. The six months after birth are filled by courtesy of his foster carer.

Tom's background information is gathered in some semblance of order and can be found underneath our bed, accessible but not threatening – something that can be brought out and dipped into in manageable doses as Tom grows and matures enough to take ownership of what is rightfully his. A garish yellow, green and white cardboard box, with a matching lid upon which is attached a piece of A4 paper with the words Tom's Life History Box and a black and white computerised picture of an owl, it accompanied Jo, unannounced, one visit. What a box. All the known pieces of his jigsaw live inside. It is one of the most precious belongings we have in our home.

We have photographs of the many people who surrounded Tom's birth mother as she grew up and yet Tom was a concealed pregnancy with very few people except Sarah and her own mother knowing of his existence pre-birth. It is a testament to, or perhaps explanation for, Tom's stubborn, strong ways that he was as healthy as he was at birth. Happy as a child, Sarah is the youngest from a second marriage. Her beloved father died tragically in an accident. Sadly, we know Sarah suffered with serious depression. There is a story there to be pieced together one day by Tom and made sense of if possible. To help him with this unenviable task, children's services asked Sarah for as much information as they could, including the name of his birth father, but to this day she maintains she does not know it. Tom's birth father was a brief acquaintance of one night who, in all probability, is unaware that he fathered a noisy, truly quite beautiful son.

Taken from *When Daisy met Tommy*, by Jules Belle, published by BAAF in 2010 (pp 14–15 and 17–18). © Jules Belle

FAMILY FINDING AND LINKING SERVICES

Children Who Wait

Adoption UK's family-finding service, *Children Who Wait*, is a secure online tool and a printed publication that features profiles of children waiting for adoption, including information on their backgrounds and needs, and in some cases online video content. Prospective adopters and their social workers can access *Children Who Wait* by joining Adoption UK; the service enables them to contact the child's (or children's) social worker directly.

Adoption UK also runs social and other events in different areas.

Adoption exchange events

Many local authority and voluntary adoption agencies and consortia join together to run "adoption exchange events". Adoption Match and the Adoption Register also run national adoption exchange events and send along representatives to local events.

The agencies (and Adoption Match and the Adoption Register) bring details, photographs and film clips of the children for whom they are looking for suitable families. Adopters who have been approved can come along and find out more about the children and may be able to chat to the children's social workers and register their interest.

The Adoption Register for England

The Adoption Register works with adoption agencies and adoption consortia to make sure that all children and families have the best chance of finding a suitable match. Its main purpose is to find adoptive homes for those children for whom local authorities cannot find a home locally. The Adoption Register is operated by Adoption Match on behalf of the Department for Education. Wales has its own Adoption Register, as do Scotland and Northern Ireland.

Agencies can refer adopters to the Adoption Register as soon as they have been approved by the agency and will usually do this if it seems unlikely that the adopters will be matched quickly with a suitable child in their own region. Agencies must refer adopters to the Adoption Register three months after they have been approved if there is not a match with an identified child being actively pursued. Adopters can also self-refer three months after they have been approved. Agencies that are referring adopters must have the adopters' consent first.

At the time of writing, the Government is currently looking at how the Adoption Register can be made more accessible for adopters.

Adoption Activity Days

Adoption Activity Days – initially piloted in the East Midlands by BAAF – are included in the Government's adoption reform agenda. These activity days, also called adoption parties by some, provide an opportunity for prospective adopters to meet, play with and talk to some children whom they would otherwise only read about or see in a video. Prospective adopters who are already approved or who have a panel date within three months can go along to these events where children who need families are brought along by their foster carers and social worker for a fun day of face-painting, crafts and play.

Linkmaker

This is an online family-finding service run by adoptive parents, which helps agencies to find adoption and fostering matches for children. Adopters and foster carers can register for family-finding and to access support. The service also has chatrooms and support groups for adopters, and information about adoption and fostering.

Visit www.linkmaker.co.uk

Something about that chubby little face called out to me...

I didn't have a pregnancy to cope with, but I did have a very long time to think about being a mum. It took two years from the time I decided to go ahead to the time when I first met Alan and took him home. My life changed in many ways during that period – moving house, commuting – outside of work my life was substantially different. To my co-workers and my friends in London, though, I must have seemed largely the same old me and I'm sure I carried on in the same old way. Getting ready to be a mother was rather like being involved in some long-term project with no particular deadline – in some ways it didn't seem as if it would ever happen.

During this lengthy build-up, I do recall having "mummy fantasies", about what it would be like to have a little person around. I could sort of envisage a life with another little person in it – after all, I'd got a room in my new house that I'd decorated for him or her. Meanwhile, when *Be My Parent* arrived each month, I scanned the pictures, feeling terrible for all the children, and hoping for some divine inspiration. When I first started chatting through things with my social worker, Sam, I just assumed that I would adopt a little girl. We had this conversation:

Sam: Have you thought about whether you'd prefer to have a girl or a boy?

Me: Yes, well I'd like a girl of course.

Sam: Why of course?

Me: I don't know really. I suppose because I feel as if I don't know anything about boys...and I'll be on my own. There won't be a male around. I just imagined it would be easier all round if I had a girl.

Sam: You know, it's funny, but I've always imagined you with a little boy.

Me: Really? Why's that?

Sam: I'm not sure, exactly. I just can see you with a little boy.

Me: Oh! Well, I hadn't really thought about having a boy. I suppose there's no harm in thinking about it.

And so I did. I thought it through and decided it was more important to find the right child, regardless of whether they were a boy or girl and then, as it happened, I spotted Alan. To this day, I'm not sure what attracted me to him. The description in *Be My Parent* was frank about his background – I read that both his parents had mental illnesses, which could have implications for him in the future. I think the main point was that Alan was a healthy, normal little boy right now, and I felt I could handle that. Also, his birthday was on the same day as my Mum's, which I felt was a bit of an omen. It also mentioned him splashing around in the sea on holiday, which conjured up such a cute picture that I couldn't help myself. My friends who've had children the normal way have often spoken about how, when they first saw their newborn babies, they kind of fell in love. Something about that chubby little face called out to me. I don't know how or why, but I knew Alan was destined to be my son the minute I clapped eyes on him!

Is this the best way to find a child a family?

Adoption parties allow hard-to-placed children to mingle with potential parents. Critics have called them 'beauty pageants' – but do they work? Kate Hilpern attends one gathering to find out.

'Weren't you tempted to bring one home?' is the most common reaction I get when I mention that I went to an adoption party last weekend. To which I've found myself honestly replying that I was tempted by a lot more than one.

To the casual onlooker, the event – which took place in a primary school in Bolton – looked like something in between a children's party and a school fete. Outside, there were bouncy castles, giant Lego and animals to pet; inside there was everything from soft play to face painting to crafts and later, after the party tea, a magic show. But behind the fun, the aim could hardly have been more serious: to get some of the 59 kids who attended out of the care system and into adoptive families.

Adoption parties – or activity days, as the British Association for Adoption and Fostering (BAAF) prefers to call them – have been going just shy of two years in the UK and the idea is simple. Invite a bunch of kids who, for various reasons (they may be in sibling groups, have disabilities, be a bit older) have been hard to place. Then invite approved adopters. Set up activities that get them doing entertaining stuff together (even the bouncy castle was chosen because adults could get on, too) and hope the adopters feel a connection and wind up adopting one of the 4,000 children who are awaiting adoption in the UK.

So far, the parties have been a hit, with 20 per cent of children adopted as a result, roughly double the rate expected by the more traditional means of matching, which usually involve social workers matching kids with adults who have never met them, using paper profiles. Crucial to their success is that there's no secrecy. Indeed, the children know it's an opportunity to meet families who want to adopt and to meet other children who need a new family, but that it might not lead to their finding a family.

'All we need now is a barbeque and a beer,' jokes one adopter nervously, as he looks up at the unexpected blue sky (rain had been forecast) and then down at a handful of kids running around with the pirate swords they have just made. Truth is, I could do with a drink, too, for there are times when it feels overwhelming to see so many children who might never get the one thing most of us take for granted – a family.

At least there's the "quiet room". This designated classroom is set aside for adopters to take a breather if it all gets too emotional, as well as to look through the booklet of profiles of children they take a shine to or talk to a social worker to learn a bit more about them.

For the most part, though, it's the excitement and magic of the day that rubs off on everyone, including me. 'This little'un has been up since 6am asking when it starts,' one foster carer says, laughing, as she watches him run round ecstatically in circles.

'Find me a child here that's not having a good time,' a social worker shouts above the noise of laughter and shouting when I'm back inside. 'It's only the adults who are nervous.' He's right, I think, looking at some of the couples gathering timidly around the edges of the room. Others get stuck in. 'It's not easy,' admits one man as he kneels down on a soft-play mat. 'Society usually discourages us from talking to kids we don't know, especially couples like us who are gay. But this is our second adoption party and we want to make use of every minute.'

Despite putting the heat back into what can feel like a detached and bureaucratic process (I should know – I sat on an adoption panel for 10 years), adoption parties have attracted controversy. A few months ago, Anne Marie Carrie, who was then the head of Barnardo's, was scornful: 'This is not Battersea Dogs Home. I am concerned about the aspect of beauty parades.' Others have labelled them speed dating for toddlers, shopping expeditions and cattle markets. Such fears are understandable. These are fragile hearts we're dealing with – kids who have probably been removed from their families due to a history of neglect or abuse. Many have had multiple foster placements and all of them will be particularly sensitive to rejection. 'What if they ask us if they can come home with us?' asks one adopter anxiously in the short briefing they got at the start of the event.

'Be honest,' says Bridget Betts, the adoption activity days programme manager at BAAF. 'Say they're going home with their foster carers.' In fact, no child does ask that, or anything like it – they rarely do, she says. They're too busy having fun and meeting other people like them, often for the first time, as well as lapping up the attention from the adults, which they tend to crave more than most kids do. 'Did you see the cupcake I just made?' or 'are you going on the bouncy castle?' were the only kinds of questions I heard them ask.

Betts doesn't deny there are risks. 'But what's the alternative? And it's not as if the children aren't well-prepared.'

The same goes for the adopters, who have several strict rules to obey, notably: no removing of the booklets from the room, no talk of adoption; meeting kids but not monopolising them. 'We once had nine sets of adopters crowding one little girl – we simply can't have that.'

What surprises so many adopters are the indirect benefits of the day. 'I came here feeling quite disillusioned about the adoption process because there's so much waiting involved,' one adopter tells me. 'But these kids and this atmosphere – it's made me feel enthused again.'

Another tells me she's approved to adopt sibling groups, but is finding herself drawn to single children. 'We were also pretty sure we wanted a boy, but I've just talked to two lovely little girls.'

In America, where these events have been part of the adoption fabric for years, adopters almost always leave with wider views about the kinds of children they could take on. 'Like many adopters, I went along to the adoption party with set ideas, in my case wanting a six to eight-year-old boy – certainly no older,' Ruth Bodian, from Boston, says. 'But then I noticed an 11-year-old boy hanging around the Disney station and we got chatting and I noticed all kinds of intangible things in his temperament and his eyes that I don't think I'd have noticed in a photo or documents about him. That was seven years ago and Jaron has been with me ever since.'

Significantly, Jaron says he felt adoption parties stopped him feeling a passive part of the family-finding process. 'I chose my mum every bit as much as she chose me and that feels good,' he says. 'You'd expect there to be a spark when you form any other kind of relationship in life. Why don't we value the chemistry in adoption, which is expected to be a lifelong relationship?'

Finally, it's time to go home. If the experts recommend a match based on the bonds formed today, these adopters could have a new family in just a few months. And it's this excitement the adults seem to leave with, no matter how apprehensive they were when they arrived.

'I've been working in adoption for 30 years and this was my first adoption party,' one social worker says after pulling me aside on my way out.

'I wasn't sure about it, but now I feel like tossing my paper profiles out of the window.' She looks so moved that she might cry.

As for the kids, it's only when a little girl trips over and grazes the arm that is clutching her party bag on the way out that I realise it's the first moment of sorrow – let alone tears – that I've seen all day among all 59 children.

About my life

When I lived with my birth family I was only 0–3 years old. I remember being with my mum's boyfriend and his sister Sally but that is really how much I remember. I still think about my mum today. She died when I was just turned three. I was sad from that day onwards.

The first time I went into foster care was when I was 15 months old because my mum was on drugs at that time and could not stop or care for me. I was very confused at the time. I was only a baby. Then I went back to my mum because she sorted herself out and could control herself. When my mum died, I had to go back into foster care because I had no one to care for me but for a little while I stayed with a lady named Helen. Then in came my dad. I lived with him for a year but he could not look after me any more. So I went to a family for a while but then I moved on to my foster family. I stayed there for two-and-a-half years.

I loved it there. It was like it was home forever. One time when I used to go and see my dad he gave me sweets and I used to irritate Josh, who is my foster brother. I used to wave them in his face. Another time, me and Millie spied on Tim. When he went to the toilet we hid in the cupboard in the bathroom.

When I was with my foster family, I saw a therapist called Rebecca. I saw her every week at a centre. One day she brought a little booklet. I was very eager to see what it was about, so she told me to open it. My foster carer Caroline read it to us. It said, 'Jade, someone wants to adopt you' and when I turned the page there was a beautiful picture of my new mum. I was over the moon about getting a new mum. I was allowed to call her 'Mum' but her real name is Rose. She was going to be my new real mum. A couple of weeks later Rose called and told my foster carer where I was going to live; she said I was going to live in London. I was happy and sad. The reason I was happy was because I got to live in London. The reason I was sad was because it was far from where I was living now, but at least I could come and visit everyone in the holidays. I knew what adoption was. Caroline explained that I would not always live with her that I would move on and find a real mum that would always be there for me.

Well, I was waiting for a very long time to get adopted and I could not wait to get adopted. It meant the world to me that I was going to have a mum that I could call 'Mum' and not have to call her by her first name. I knew that I was going to be in the adoption newspaper but when I found out I had a mum I did not know that they had put me in it already! I was very joyful when Caroline told me that I was up for adoption. I wanted a family with other older children but it ended up that I did not get a brother or a sister, I just got a mum but I was still overjoyed about this big drama that was happening.

I was helped to pack. I knew when I was moving and what day I would be going. We got a lot of cardboard boxes for all my toys and books. It felt a bit strange moving my stuff again. It was another big journey that I was going on.

A couple of days later I was about to meet my new mum for the first time! I felt like a total bag of nerves to meet my new and true mum. That day when I was at school, I drew a picture for her to say that I already loved her. The day I met her all my friends and teachers wished me the best of luck, that this was the right mum for me, they just knew it in their blood. I came into the room with my foster sister and there was my new mum, Rose, sitting on the comfy sofa. She had made herself at home in seconds. We talked about what we would do in London, like go on the London Eye, see the Houses of Parliament and, most importantly, Big Ben.

We met a couple of times. The second day was the weekend so we went shopping in town. We went to Woolworths, Roy's, Stead and Simpson's and the grocery store to get some strawberries and oranges. The third day we took Rose to our church. She really liked our church. She said it was much bigger than her church. The night before we left to go to London for the first time I had my mum's car keys. I opened her boot and threw the keys in the back of her boot and slammed the door shut. The reason I put the keys in the boot was because I did not want to leave. The next day Rose asked me if I knew where her keys had gone and I said nothing. I ran upstairs as fast as my legs could go. She called the AA and they came and we were off in no time. I cried a river of tears; that was how much I did not want to leave!

The best things about being adopted though is that you get to go to adoption parties, meet new people and children and go out to places for a couple of nights. When I went to Peterborough camping everyone was adopted, we collected wood from the dusty forest and gathered around the campfire.

We have also been to France with our local adoption group. That was amazing. We spoke in French. We ate French food. It was delightful.

But the worst thing about being adopted is everyone wants to know what happened, what it feels like and they always say, 'I feel sorry for you', and go all soppy. I was very sad when I had to change schools because I had made loads of new friends and then I was moved. I was really upset because I had to leave my best friend behind called Cameron but I stay in contact with her. But I moved to a very good school. I had friends in no time. My best friend is Alanna. She came in Year 5.

Well, my name is Jade. I am from Essex. I am ten-and-a-half. I live in London. I'm in my last year at primary which is Year 6. I love animals. I have a dog and a hamster and might get a rabbit. I like loads about myself. I am a world traveller. I have been to New Zealand, Africa-Tanzania, Scotland, New York and France.

I feel really happy when it is Christmas because you get loads of nice presents and you celebrate Jesus's birthday. I also feel super happy when it is my birthday because I get to be a new number, like next year I am going to be 11 years old. I feel a bit sad when it's Mother's Day because I never made my mum a card but this year I did and I put it in my small garden so she could see it, from heaven.

The thing about my family is they are from different countries but my adopted family are just from England. My nan is from Ireland. My granddad is from Pakistan and I do not know where my dad is from.

By Jade, aged 10, reproduced from *The Colours in Me*, edited by Perlita Harris, published by BAAF in 2008 (p 11). © BAAF

The kind of child I think I could adopt

....
....
....
....
....
....
....
....
....
....
....
....
....
....
....
....
....
....
....
....
....
....
....
....

MODULE 3: **The adoption process**

Learning outcomes

This session aims to help you to:

- **understand what the journey to adoption will involve**
- **understand the assessment process and why it is necessary**
- **understand more about how children and adopters are matched with each other**
- **understand why adopters may need support, both at the start and in the long term**

Ten steps to becoming an adoptive parent

After you have applied to adopt, the main steps of the adoption process for prospective adopters are:

1 You attend preparation sessions.

2 Checks, references and a medical are arranged and carried out.

3 A social worker carries out an assessment (also called "home study").

4 The report written by your social worker about you – the Prospective Adopter's Report – is given to an adoption panel for their recommendation of your approval as prospective adopters. The agency makes the final decision.

5 If you are approved, the social workers consider a match between you and a child who has been authorised for adoption by a placement order or a section 19 parental consent. The social worker from the child's agency sends you the Child's Permanence Report and arranges to meet you to discuss the proposed match. If it is agreed that the match will proceed, the child's agency must assess your and the child's support needs and agree a support plan with you.

6 An adoption panel considers the proposed match, makes a recommendation and advises on contact, adoption support and exercise of parental responsibilities. The child's local authority then makes a decision to proceed with the match.

7 You and the child are introduced.

8 The child moves in (i.e. is placed with you).

9 An adoption order is made through the court.

10 You can request an assessment of your post-adoption support needs.

Reproduced from *The Adopter's Handbook* by Amy Neil Salter, published by BAAF in 2013 (pp 20–21).
© Amy Neil Salter

EXPLORING WHAT ADOPTION WILL MEAN

Worksheets

During Stage One of your adoption assessment, it is important that you begin to explore what adoption will mean for you and your family. In addition to any preparation and training you attend, it is helpful for you to start to think about the areas of your life that you will be asked to talk about and discuss with your assessing social worker during the home study assessment in Stage Two. The following worksheets (reproduced from *Undertaking an Adoption Assessment*, Dibben, 2013) can be used for you to start to record your contributions to this work and it is hoped will also help you reflect on what has brought you to the point of adoption and what you will be bringing to your role as an adoptive parent. There are no right answers, and your assessing social worker will be able to go over all this information with you during the assessment in Stage Two, so if you are finding some things difficult to write, make a note of them so you can discuss them with your agency.

The worksheets link to the sections of the assessment report that your social worker will complete at the end of your assessment. You may find that as you attend some training, your views may change, so you can always revisit or add to the worksheets before you share them with a social worker.

These forms should be available from your agency or they may have devised their own. You can complete them electronically or you use them as a guide to write your own response.

Your family

This worksheet focuses on your childhood experiences, how they have shaped you as a person and what you are bringing from these experiences into your role as an adoptive parent. (If a couple, to be completed separately by each of you.)

- Family tree/genogram – Complete a family tree/genogram using the template as a guide, going back to your grandparents (with dates of birth and whether family members are living or deceased) and including other significant family members.
- Where were you born and brought up?
- Give details of who was in your family and any other people who were important to you during your childhood and describe your relationships with them.
- Describe your experience of childhood – what are your positive memories and were there any periods of difficulty, e.g. periods of separation, illness, family breakdown, bereavement that impacted on you? How were these difficult times dealt with and who supported you through those times?
- What were your adolescent years like? Were there any significant times?
- How do you think your experiences as a child have shaped the person you are today?
- What is your relationship like now with your parents and any brothers and sisters? How have your relationships with them changed over time?
- What have been the significant events in your adult life?
- What has given you the greatest satisfaction in your life so far and what has been the biggest regret or disappointment?
- How would you describe your personality now – what do you feel are your strengths and is there anything you would like to change?
- How would other people who are close to you describe you?

Your education

This worksheet looks at your experience of school and education, how this has influenced your views on the importance of education and how you will help a child reach their potential.

- List the schools and any further education you attended in the chronology template. What were your exam results or qualifications?
- What was your experience of the schools you attended? Did you experience any additional changes in your schooling? How was this managed by you and your parents?
- How did your parents support you in your education? Was there anything you wish they had done differently?
- Have you completed any education or training as an adult? Do you have any plans to complete any further training or qualifications?
- What do you see as being important about education and training now as a parent/prospective adopter?
- What hopes or expectations would you have of the education of any child being placed with you? How would you support them? If you have children, what has your experience been as a parent of the schools and teaching your children have received?

Your employment

When a child is placed with you, you may be balancing your work commitments with parenting or adjusting to not working. It is helpful for us to know what your existing work patterns are and how you expect these to change after placement.

- Give details of your current and previous employment from leaving school to the present day in the chronology template.
- Tell us about your experience of work – have you worked with children or in a caring situation? Have you had any periods of time when you were not working?
- What was your parents' attitude to work? How did this influence you?
- What are your future plans – are you planning to change your work patterns or leave work when a child is placed? How will this affect your lifestyle and any friendships or support you receive through work?
- If you are intending to continue work or change your patterns of working, what impact will this have on you and what plans do you have for covering child care during school holidays or when a child is ill?
- How will your work commitments fit with your role as an adoptive parent? Have you discussed this with your employer and are they supportive of your plans? What are your employer's policies on statutory adoption leave and statutory adoption pay and will you be able to make use of these entitlements?

Adult life

Your health

Your views and attitudes to health as a parent will be important, as a child placed with you may have particular health conditions. This information will add to the information gathered as part of your adoption medical.

- What do you do to try to maintain a healthy lifestyle? Would you do anything differently if you had a child?
- Do you or any member of your family have any illnesses or health conditions, and if so, how does that impact on your/their life? Would these conditions have any impact on you parenting a child?
- What support do you have from other people to help you manage any ongoing health issues, including health professionals?

Any cautions and convictions

Previous offences will not prevent you from being an adoptive parent, but it will be helpful to understand the circumstances and your reflections now on what happened.

- If you have received any cautions or convictions during your childhood or as an adult, can you explain the circumstances that led to the incident/s, how they were dealt with and any sentences given through the court?
- How do you now reflect on the incident/s and what changes did you make following them?
- How would you explain this to any child placed with you and how would you deal with them if they became involved in any offending behaviour?

Significant previous partners

Your experience with your previous partners may have influenced you in different ways and they may still have a role or some involvement in your life now, so it is helpful to have some understanding of any significant relationships and how you have reflected on them. Where there were children involved, it is helpful to understand your involvement with them then and now.

For each significant partnership

- Describe the relationship, how long it lasted and why it ended. What were the positives and were there any negatives about the relationship? Do you have any contact now with your ex-partner? What do you feel you learned from the relationship?
- If there were any children in or from the relationship, who did the children live with after the relationship ended and how was this decided? What contact was agreed and how does it work for everyone?
- How much do these children and their other parent know about your adoption application and what do they think about it? How will you make sure that you can meet these children's needs alongside those of the child/ren placed with you?

Your current relationship

Adopting a child, like parenthood generally, can add an extra dimension to your relationship and you will be a great source of support to each other so it is helpful to understand how your relationship has developed and how you work together as a team.

- Describe how, where and when you met and how your relationship developed.
- What do each of you feel makes your relationship work? What roles do each of you have in the

relationship and in your household? How do you make decisions as a couple? Can you give some examples of this?

- What do you see as the strengths of your relationship? How has your relationship developed over time?
- What has been the most difficult thing you have been through as a couple and how did you support each other through this? Were there things you would change or have changed as a result of this experience?
- How do you think adopting a child will impact on or change your relationship?
- Where do you see yourselves in 20 years' time?
- If you are adopting alone but you have a partner, how much will they be involved with the child and how do they see their role?
- If you don't have a partner at present, how would you ensure that your adopted child was supported if you have any relationships in the future?

Members of your household

Other adults living in your family are likely to play an important role in the life of your adopted child so we need to understand something about them, their views about you adopting and how involved they will be with a child. Any children you have will have their lives changed by a new brother or sister joining the family and it is helpful to know more about them and how you have prepared them for these changes.

- Are there any other adults living in your home? If so, give details of who they are and your relationship with them. What role would they have with any child placed with you?
- If you have any children living with you or living elsewhere, describe their personality and character, interests and talents.
- What is their relationship like with any brothers and sisters they have? How might this change if another child/ren joins the family?
- How are they doing at nursery/school/college?
- What do they understand about adoption and why children need to be adopted?
- If any of your children are adopted, what has been their experience of adoption? How do you think they will cope with any differences in the circumstances of another child joining the family, e.g. different contact arrangements, family backgrounds, etc?
- How have your children been involved in your plans to adopt? What have been their views and have these changed over time?
- How do you think they will benefit from an adopted child joining the family? Are there any areas where they might be vulnerable, and if so, how would you manage this?

Your support network

Adopting a child will bring some challenges, and there are times when having support from family and friends, both practical and emotional, can help adopters have time for themselves and each other or talk through things that are happening and how they are feeling. It helps to think through who will be available to offer you this support and how much you will involve them in learning and understanding about what adoption is going to involve.

- Ecomap: Complete an ecomap/diagram based on the template provided, showing all the people you know who you think will be offering you emotional or practical support. You may want to include membership groups, churches or professionals who you think will be a support to you. (There is a sample of a family support map and a genogram at the end of this module.)

- Tell us something about the main people who you think will support you and what kind of support they will give you.
- Are there times when you have needed to call on them for support in the past – can you give some examples of this?
- What do your family and friends think about you adopting? Are there any family members or friends who have expressed concerns about you adopting a child? Have you thought about how you will manage this so it does not have a negative impact on you or your child?
- Are you involved in any local groups or organisations? Are people there aware of your plans to adopt and how do you feel they will support you?
- Do you know any other adopters, foster carers or people who are adopted? What support might you receive from them? Would you think about using support groups for adopters before or after your child is placed with you?

Your home

- Describe your home and any garden or play areas and the space you have for a child joining your family.
- Do you own your home or is it a rented property? If rented, how secure is your tenancy and is the landlord aware of your plan to adopt? How long you have lived here?
- Are there any changes you need to make to your home so it is suitable for children? If so, what is your timescale for getting these done?
- Use the health and safety checklist provided to think about any further changes you will need to make to your home in preparation for a child being placed with you.
- Have you any plans to move house in the future? What would the implications of this be for a child being placed with you?
- If you have pets tell us about them, how they respond to children and any issues you think might arise for your child or your pet with a child joining the family. Your agency may ask you to complete a questionnaire to help you think about this.

Your local community and leisure interests

- Tell us about your town, village and the area that you live in and what is available for children in your area (e.g. schools, health, leisure facilities). If any of these are not within your local area, where can they be found and what transport is available?
- How involved are you in your local community? Do you attend local groups or activities? What makes it a suitable area for children?
- What interests or hobbies do you enjoy? How much time does this take up? Do you do any of these with your partner (where applicable) and are there some activities you would want to involve a child in? Will you need to make any changes to these after a child joins your family?

Your lifestyle

These prompts are to help you think about your life as it is now and how it is likely to change when a child joins your family.

- Describe a typical weekend in your household.
- Describe your routine during the week.
- How do you think a child joining your family will impact on the things that you and any other family members are involved in? What might need to change?
- Who does what in your family, e.g. cooking, cleaning, etc? Are these roles important to you?
- Are there any "house rules" that exist in your home or that you think you would introduce for a child joining your family?
- What is your attitude to food and mealtimes? How would you manage a child who had difficulties with food?
- What leisure activities do you and any other family members enjoy individually and as a family?
- Are there any religious or cultural practices that are important in your household? How would this change when a child joins your family?
- How do you celebrate special occasions (birthdays/religious festivals/Christmas/anniversaries)?
- What kind of holidays do you enjoy? How might this change when a child is placed?

Reproduced from *Undertaking an Adoption Assessment*, by Elaine Dibben, published by BAAF in 2013 (pp 70–80). © BAAF

ON THE ASSESSMENT PROCESS/HOME STUDY

Like free therapy

[The home study] was relatively painless. Our social worker was nothing short of brilliant. It felt like having free therapy at times! In time, she turned into more of a good friend, even part of the family, rather than being just a social worker, and we can feel too that she is extremely fond of us, as we're her first gay adoptive couple.

Also, we'd been through a similar vetting process before we started providing supported lodgings to homeless gay teenagers via the Albert Kennedy Trust, so we were quite used to the nature of questions being asked and the process of evaluation, in many ways.

If anything, this process felt more streamlined even though it was more in-depth, largely due to the more stringent government guidelines surrounding adoption and our social worker's efficiency at her job.

From *The Pink Guide to Adoption for Lesbians and Gay Men*, by Nicola Hill, published by BAAF in 2012 (pp 193–194). © Nicola Hill

The veggie thing was just too important

Anna arrived at eight one dark, autumnal night. She was half an hour late, having got lost on the country roads in the dark, sat politely on the edge of our armchair and looked a bit uncomfortable. She sorted through her paperwork for a few minutes and then looked at us both.

'I suppose you want to know what I'm here for.'

And that was the start of it. During that first two-hour encounter we chit-chatted our way to getting to know each other. David and I sat hand-in-hand on the sofa; Anna gradually sank down into the armchair, as she relaxed a little. I couldn't make the puppy sit in the kitchen all that time, so had him asleep at my feet. Anna was impressed: we'd passed the initial "Is the dog safe?" test. We spent twenty minutes just looking at our diaries and trying to work out how often and how quickly we could get the six or so meetings out of the way. We also talked very generally about our work situations, but everything would have to be examined in minute detail in subsequent weeks. This woman would help to determine whether or not we could have a child; she would have to ask us very personal questions and would have to discuss matters we hadn't even disclosed to our families or close friends. I was very worried that I wouldn't like her. She was quite matter-of-fact and sometimes seemed to look through us. Was she bored? Did she understand our answers?

Within three weeks we had three lengthy meetings with her. We went through the agency's assessment form, paragraph by paragraph. Designed to capture a picture of us as prospective parents, it would be used to match us with a particular child. We covered family histories, described our own childhoods, and agreed that love, stability and opportunities were the three words we chose to take from our own backgrounds to use as parents. We weren't finding this a difficult process. Some prospective adopters have unsupportive families, difficult relationships with ex-wives, ex-husbands, and ex-lovers. And although our support network proved to be a bit tricky, as most of our friends live far away, the geographical proximity of our respective parents was crucial. We talked about ethnicity: how would we feel about having a child of dual heritage placed with us, and what, if anything, could we offer them? We discussed the problems we were not ready to take on, such as severe disabilities or children with a short life expectancy. We talked about the house and Anna saw where a child would sleep. And then we looked at behavioural issues. What would we be worst or best at? What about discipline? What would be challenging? We got to the part in the assessment form where it mentions food and our approach to it. We could have said anything, and Anna was probably looking for phrases like "balanced diet" and "family meals", which we uttered in due course. But as vegetarians for over twenty years it was an important issue for us, and we decided to be explicit about our plans to bring up our child as a vegetarian too.

Anna looked slightly uncomfortable. What about the full range of food groups? Vitamins? Societal acceptance? We'd given all this much thought and responded readily. But then she queried how a child would cope with the transition to vegetarian food. We would want our baby to feel as little disruption as possible, so I assured her that I would happily cook meat look-alikes if he or she had been eating meat in the foster home. Anna seemed to throw up obstacle after obstacle. Maybe she was testing us? Maybe she wanted to see how deeply rooted this "principle" was?

She left a bit early that evening and we grumbled about her for a few days afterwards. We did realise that the transition period can be very hard: children may have been moved a number of times already before they arrive at the adoptive home – what they need is stability. On the preparation course we met a couple of adopters who took on a five-year-old girl and, as if to compensate for a life she hadn't enjoyed up to that point, almost immediately went on holiday to Wales with her. They laughed over the total and utter disaster, but said it had been very traumatic at the time. This child didn't need holidays, didn't need to be overwhelmed by endless visitors coming to meet the new arrival. She just needed tranquility and time to trust her new mum and dad when they said that she wouldn't be moved again. After all, for her car journeys meant upheaval, not just a trip to the supermarket. So we were aware of the implications, but decided that the veggie thing was just too important for us to let go.

From *Take Two*, by Laurel Ashton, published by BAAF in 2008 (pp 58–60). © Laurel Ashton

Stage Two

So, Stage Two. Where to start? Well, as each local authority and each voluntary adoption agency seems to take a slightly different approach towards the new adoption process, I'll simply share a motley collection of my own thoughts and experiences, starting with the home study.

By using the term "home study" I mean the interviews, discussions, questionnaires and homework that together form the process whereby a social worker assesses you (and your partner and family if relevant). In case anyone is seeking ideas as to what *may* happen, here's my story.

I think I had six assessment meetings with the social worker. They were long compared to the norm, as far as I can tell – most often a full 9am 1pm morning, give or take half an hour. I typed up details of all the lovely people in my support network – pages of it that then needed thinning down. (My very local support network has been, and indeed remains, one of the areas I am conscious I need to work on...but the support of my friends and family has been and continues to be amazing and unstinting.)

I think the experience of actually going through the assessment process – or Stage Two, or home study, or whatever it is called in your area – is a very personal one. I know many feel that it's very intrusive; others feel deeply fascinated as they learn more about themselves and gain huge insights into their own past; some find out more about their partner's childhood toy preferences than they ever realised they didn't want to know! As a singleton, it was of course all about me, which mostly I found just bizarre. In any normal world, talking about yourself almost non-stop for four hours would be considered the height of un-empathetic, selfish, egotistical self-absorption. During assessment, if that's what happens you're probably doing it right! The knowledge my social worker has of me and my life, having asked me to discuss everything from my view on certain types of child health concerns to my experience of paternal discipline as a child, is greater than almost anyone else's. My knowledge of her and her life is minimal. It all feels just very odd!

My social worker was appropriately probing at times, but her empathy and willingness to listen – combined with her readiness to say quite clearly, 'That's fine, I've got enough on that' when I was waffling on (as is all-too-often my way) – meant that we seemed to zoom along. I slowly realised quite how crucial the individual personality and approach taken by your social worker is, how much of a difference it can make how they relate to you...and, of course, how the person you are yourself enables that relationship to build its own dynamic.

Individual, personal, thoughtful, dynamic relationships are the bread and butter of all the complex interwoven relationships that adoption processes and parenting entail; that the relationship between the potential adopter and the social worker is deeply personal and responsive to the individuals involved is surely right. I feel my social worker is very different from me but not only have we have got on well and (I would say) developed a good rapport, my referees also all told me they thought she had me sussed!

Finally, we reached the point five or six weeks before my approval panel was scheduled. Effectively, I had been reading and thinking and preparing and talking for months by now. In a final flurry of urgent activity, I saw and proofread a draft of the PAR (Prospective Adopter Report) and then a second draft. I signed a sheet of paper (not actually attached to the PAR at that moment, mind you, due to time running out!) saying it was all accurate. I drafted a profile for myself overnight. And a couple of days later the same again, as I quickly sent through some comments on my own learning during the process which we'd forgotten were needed. There was a pause, then I received a summons to the Post Office in the next town, and following a probably unidentifiable scrawl, I was in possession of my very own copy of this all-important document that felt as if it was going to determine my whole future.

Suddenly then it was calm. The last month before panel proved to be a strange interlude.

Your PAR is done. You may still have things to do if you've been asked to get stuff sorted – for example, get more childcare experience. I finally caught up with a single adopter I hadn't spoken to before, as well as chatting to friends of friends about their approval panel. You can, of course, keep on reading and thinking and exploring.

Ultimately, however, there is very little you can actually *do*.

What I decided, therefore, was that I would aim to do nice things. I was extremely lucky to manage a weekend away with a friend who herself is a mummy but wangled a weekend exeat. For three amazing days we wandered and talked and explored and just had the best time ever. Huge thanks to her and to her husband too! I did some babysitting – usually an excuse in my world to catch up with friends as well as see their children. I spent time appreciating lie-ins and leaving the house on a whim with just keys and cash. I walked the canal and sang along to music I chose in the car. I enjoyed sitting in silence. As ever, my family and friends were amazing and kept me boosted and smiling throughout.

This article began life as one of a series of adoption posts on Emma Long's blog, written as Pedalling Solo. For more insights, anecdotes and bewildering adventures from Emma's adoption journey visitwww.pedallingsolo. wordpress.com

ON ADOPTION SUPPORT

- The statutory new "Adoption Passport" sets out the support that adopters in England may be entitled to in matters relating to the child's education, and entitlements available to adopters including adoption leave and pay, priority for council housing, and any others; see www. first4adoption.org.uk.
- Adopters have the right to have their needs for support assessed – however, there is currently no

duty on the local authority to *provide* this support to any individual adopter. Provision of services will depend on the adopters' circumstances.

- Future changes in the law mean that those receiving adoption support will be able to decide how it is provided, either by local authorities or through a "personal budget" to purchase services from a voluntary adoption agency or adoption support agency. An Adoption Support Fund was established in 2015.

- The local authority that places the child is responsible for assessing and (where appropriate) providing adoption support services for three years after the adoption order is made. After three years, this becomes the responsibility of the local authority where the adopters live (if this is different from the placing authority). The exception is that financial support and any contact arrangements agreed by the placing authority before the adoption order is made remain the responsibility of the placing authority.

Genogram example: Robert and Jyoti

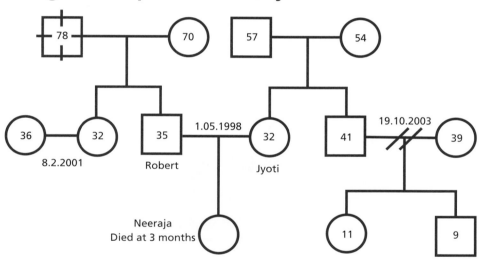

Genogram symbols

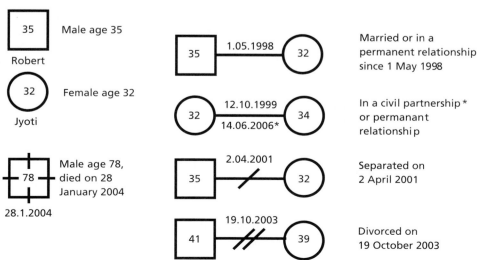

Family support map example

Applicants provide a visual map of their support network with particular reference to adoption. They should indicate who their main supporters are (the emphasis should be on identifying the quality of contacts – it is not a popularity contest!). Applicants indicate their relationship to the supporters (including how long known), their location, how often they are in contact and what form of contact this takes. Attitude to adoption and ability to provide support should be indicated. Ethnicity/faith/culture should be indicated as the supporters may be an important resource or role model for a child (in the event of their being placed outside their own community). This can also be an indicator of the extent to which applicants have integrated people with other experiences and backgrounds into their lives so far. The supporters' proximity in the map should indicate the significance of the relationship. Spaces can be created for support that is not yet in place, but which the applicants actively expect to develop in the future.

Present support which will be available post-placement:

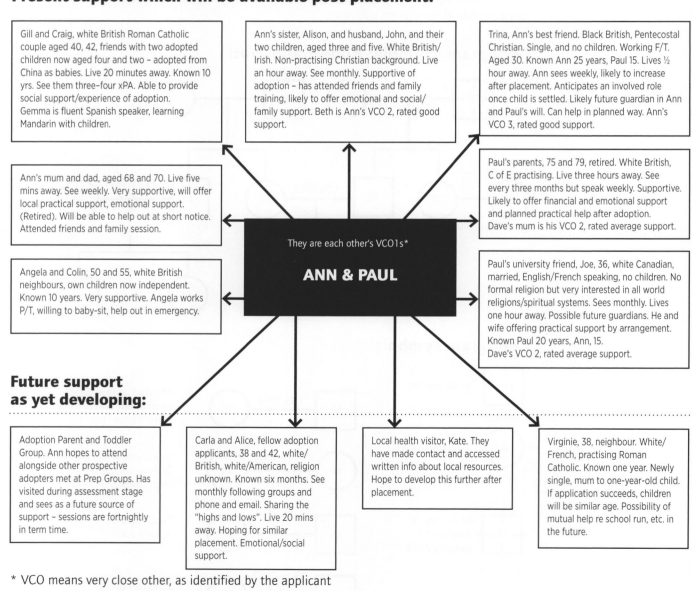

Gill and Craig, white British Roman Catholic couple aged 40, 42, friends with two adopted children now aged four and two – adopted from China as babies. Live 20 minutes away. Known 10 yrs. See them three–four xPA. Able to provide social support/experience of adoption. Gemma is fluent Spanish speaker, learning Mandarin with children.

Ann's sister, Alison, and husband, John, and their two children, aged three and five. White British/Irish. Non-practising Christian background. Live an hour away. See monthly. Supportive of adoption – has attended friends and family training, likely to offer emotional and social/family support. Beth is Ann's VCO 2, rated good support.

Trina, Ann's best friend. Black British, Pentecostal Christian. Single, and no children. Working F/T. Aged 30. Known Ann 25 years, Paul 15. Lives ½ hour away. Ann sees weekly, likely to increase after placement. Anticipates an involved role once child is settled. Likely future guardian in Ann and Paul's will. Can help in planned way. Ann's VCO 3, rated good support.

Ann's mum and dad, aged 68 and 70. Live five mins away. See weekly. Very supportive, will offer local practical support, emotional support. (Retired). Will be able to help out at short notice. Attended friends and family session.

Paul's parents, 75 and 79, retired. White British, C of E practising. Live three hours away. See every three months but speak weekly. Supportive. Likely to offer financial and emotional support and planned practical help after adoption. Dave's mum is his VCO 2, rated average support.

They are each other's VCO1s*

ANN & PAUL

Angela and Colin, 50 and 55, white British neighbours, own children now independent. Known 10 years. Very supportive. Angela works P/T, willing to baby-sit, help out in emergency.

Paul's university friend, Joe, 36, white Canadian, married, English/French speaking, no children. No formal religion but very interested in all world religions/spiritual systems. Sees monthly. Lives one hour away. Possible future guardians. He and wife offering practical support by arrangement. Known Paul 20 years, Ann, 15. Dave's VCO 2, rated average support.

Future support as yet developing:

Adoption Parent and Toddler Group. Ann hopes to attend alongside other prospective adopters met at Prep Groups. Has visited during assessment stage and sees as a future source of support – sessions are fortnightly in term time.

Carla and Alice, fellow adoption applicants, 38 and 42, white/British, white/American, religion unknown. Known six months. See monthly following groups and phone and email. Sharing the "highs and lows". Live 20 mins away. Hoping for similar placement. Emotional/social support.

Local health visitor, Kate. They have made contact and accessed written info about local resources. Hope to develop this further after placement.

Virginie, 38, neighbour. White/French, practising Roman Catholic. Known one year. Newly single, mum to one-year-old child. If application succeeds, children will be similar age. Possibility of mutual help re school run, etc. in the future.

* VCO means very close other, as identified by the applicant
Adapted with permission from Surrey County Council

MODULE 4: **Children's development and attachment**

Learning outcomes

This module aims to help you understand more about:

- children's developmental needs
- impact of adversity in early life
- importance of attachment for babies and children
- how bonds of attachment are formed
- what can go wrong in attachment
- children's identity needs

ON ATTACHMENT

Definitions

Attachment: The feeling/need a child has for a particular adult or small group of adults.

Bonding: The process by which an adult grows to love a child.

Attachment behaviour: The things which a child does to get an adult to respond and stay close, e.g. crying, smiling, gurgling, following.

The function of attachment behaviour is protection plus physical and emotional survival. Unlike other primate infants, human babies cannot physically cling to or follow their parent so must develop an alternative way of keeping the parent close. Attachment is also key in helping a baby to begin to learn how to regulate emotion.

The importance of attachment

Attachment has been defined as 'an affectionate bond between two individuals that endures through space and time and serves to join them emotionally'.[1] When children have a strong attachment to a parent, it allows them to develop both trust for others and self-reliance. These earliest relationships influence both physical and intellectual development as well as forming the foundation for psychological development. The child's earliest attachments become the prototype for subsequent interpersonal relationships. Below are presented the many positive long-term effects of a child's strong, healthy attachment to parents. Many children who enter foster care are in jeopardy of losing some or all of these strengths.

The positive effects of attachment

A strong attachment can enable a child to:

- attain his/her full intellectual potential
- sort out what he/she perceives
- think logically
- develop social emotions

- develop a conscience
- trust others
- become self-reliant
- cope better with stress and frustration
- reduce feelings of jealousy
- overcome common fears and worries
- increase feelings of self-worth

A child who is well attached to one carer can more easily develop attachments to others. We see this in families as the infant extends attachments to other members of the nuclear family such as the other parent and siblings. The fact that a child's strong attachment to one person eases the development of attachments to others is a crucial one for foster care. It means that children can be helped to become attached to a foster carer, and then to extend that attachment to birth family members, adoptive parents, or others. Rutter points out that if "mothering" is of high quality and provided by figures who remain the same during the child's early life, then at least up to four, or five multiple parenting figures need have no adverse effects.[2] However, young children, unlike adults, are unable to maintain strong attachments to a number of different individuals who have little connection to each other or who might be hostile to each other.[3] Although attachments can be extended to include others and can even, with the co-operation of previous parenting figures, be transferred to new carers, interruptions in parenting caused by separation and loss universally carry a measure of harm.

Parents are responsible for creating the environment that helps children achieve their maximum potential in terms of physical, intellectual, and psychological development. The child's job is to make use of the environment. Neither can accomplish the other's work; it is only in the context of the parent–child relationship that the child is able to move successfully through the stages of child development.

Studies of children raised in institutions have shown that adequate physical care is not enough to lead to the development of a physically and psychologically healthy child with optimum intellectual functioning. For normal development to occur, the child needs a primary attachment object. This person, who responds to the child's needs and who initiates positive activities with the child, seems to be indispensable for normal development. The process of engaging in lively social interactions with a child and responding readily to his or her signals and approaches is called "mothering". It does not so much matter who this individual is as long as there is someone who meets these needs.

Bowlby has noted that the securely attached child with positive expectations of self and others is more likely to approach the world with confidence. When faced with potentially alarming situations, the child is likely to tackle them effectively or to seek help in doing so.

In contrast, those infants whose emotional needs have not been consistently met respond to the world either by shrinking from it or doing battle with it.[4] Children securely attached as infants are more resilient, independent, compliant, empathic and socially competent than others. They have greater self-esteem and express more positive affect and less negative affect than do children who were anxiously attached as infants.[5]

Families as facilitators of attachment

The majority of infants are able to form attachments with any carer. This person may be a birth parent, a foster carer or adoptive parent, or even a sibling. Neither blood ties to the child nor the sex of the primary carer seem to be as important as the connections this person develops with the child. A key factor seems to be the carer's sensitivity to the baby's signals. However, when the carer initiates a variety of interactions, as opposed to only providing routine care, the attachments become stronger. Mothers and fathers usually respond to infants differently. In general, fathers are more physical and stimulating while mothers are more verbal and soothing. Yogman believes that the mother's and father's roles do not have to be interchangeable or identical; there are advantages to having them be reciprocal.[6]

In most societies the infant and his/her primary carer are members of a larger unit, the family. The family's sense of entitlement and empowerment in raising the child is usually supported by society as a whole, although either internal or external factors may inhibit the sense of entitlement. For example, American and British cultures, amongst others, have traditionally identified birth parents as more entitled to the child than anyone else, even if they are not themselves providing for the child. Two important aspects of adoption are the legal empowerment of the adoptive family and their developing sense of entitlement to parent their adopted child.[7]

The family provides the environment in which attachments with the child can grow. Below, we highlight the functions of the family in relation to children. Obviously, at different times in an individual's life, the relative importance of these tasks varies.

What families provide:

- a primary carer for the child
- care by specific adults to whom the child can become attached
- continuous contact with these adults on a day-to-day basis
- gradually changing relationships with a small number of individuals over a lifetime
- safety and security
- stimulation and encouragement for growth
- reasonable expectations
- experience in identifying and expressing emotions
- support in times of stress
- others with whom to share successes

Although a primary carer seems to be critical for normal development during early life, it is the continuous but constantly changing contact with a small number of individuals that is an especially important aspect of identity formation. Long-term relationships indicate that growth and change are possible. Relationships are not static. Normal parent–child interactions gradually change throughout their lifetime together. Even the relationship between parent and infant is different from that between adult carer and toddler.

As the child heads off to school when about five years old, the parent must be able to encourage the child to be less dependent and less exclusive in his or her relationships. When the young person becomes a teenager, and again when the adolescent leaves home, relationships change in fairly dramatic ways. In most families we do not think of contact between parent and young adult offspring ceasing when the latter leaves home. Family relationships continue to change when the young adults become parents of the next generation. Many people, upon reaching middle age, find themselves meeting more and more of their parents' dependency needs. Indeed, eventually the adult "children" may become the carers for their own elderly parents, thus completing the cycle.

These long-term relationships identify the strongest attachments. The continually changing nature of such lifetime bonds helps individuals achieve a strong sense of identity, self-worth, and responsibility. People who lack long-term attachments may have more difficulty sorting out what to attribute to their own actions and what to ascribe to changes in the environment.

Providing physical and psychological safety and security is a basic parental task for carers of the young child. The importance of this gradually diminishes as the young person becomes more capable and self-reliant. As we will see in this chapter, stimulation and encouragement for change and growth are major determinants in children achieving their intellectual potential. The freedom to explore and try new things must constantly be balanced by the family having reasonable expectations for the child and placing limits which will protect the child from serious harm while helping with the learning of social skills.

Although few parents would think of including helping the child identify and express emotions as a family responsibility, it is primarily within the family unit that the child learns these skills. In general, schools focus on what the child is not to do. Parents, especially through modelling, teach the child whether or not certain feelings are acceptable in this family, and how they may be expressed. Finally, family members are the ones with whom most individuals want to share their successes. Likewise, most turn to relatives for support in times of stress.

The development of attachment and bonding between child and parent

Parent–child relationships are usually reciprocal. Adults certainly influence the child, yet even infants have an impact on their carers. Winnicott in the 1950s noted that there is no such thing as a "baby".[8] There is only a "mother and child couple". Forming relationships, even in the earliest days of life, is cyclical – adult and infant each influencing the actions of the other.

However, there are circumstances where reciprocity is not present in a particular parent–child dyad. Either parent or child may be unresponsive to the other. One member of the pair may feel connected to the other without the reverse being true. Therefore, for clarity of communication, in this book *attachment* will be used to describe the child's connection to the parent or others while the term *bonding* will be used to describe the parent's link to the child.

In general, well-attached children have parents who are securely bonded to them. However, in some situations a parent may be bonded to a child who is not well attached because the child has difficulty forming normal relationships. An extreme example of this occurs in childhood autism, a condition in which the child has problems forming close interpersonal relationships with anyone. Yet the parents of the autistic child are usually initially well bonded to their child, and only through time modify interactions with this baby as the child's lack of responsiveness influences the adult behaviours. In other cases we find children who are actively seeking approval and love from parents who, for a variety of reasons, are not well bonded to them. In the child care system there are a significant number of cases in which bonding and attachment do not seem to go hand in hand.

Setting the stage for bonding

Between conception and birth the stage is set for bonding between parents and child. During this time, parents begin to develop images of what the unborn child will be like.

They form expectations and hopes for their child, for themselves as parents, and for their future relationship with the child. The mother and unborn child have a unique relationship with the child being dependent upon the mother's body for all nutrients, while the mother's body undergoes many hormonal and physical changes in providing for the unborn child.

Klaus and Kennel[9] identify two adaptive tasks for the mother during pregnancy: the first is to identify the foetus as an integral part of herself; the second is to become aware of the foetus as a separate individual. The latter is usually associated with foetal movement. This is when parental fantasies of the child usually start. How the mother cares for herself during the prenatal period has a profound impact on the development of the unborn child.

Unfortunately, prenatal neglect and abuse are not uncommon in our society. Irrespective of whether or not the baby and birth mother have an opportunity to develop a relationship after the infant's birth, their interdependency during the pregnancy and birth processes leads to an interpersonal connection which cannot be duplicated in any other form of relationship.

Events during the prenatal period may affect the kind of relationship that will develop between parent and child. These factors include features of the pregnancy itself, such as the timing, the mother's condition during the pregnancy, and the presence or absence of prenatal complications. Both neglect – defined as not providing for the child's basic needs – and abuse – defined as providing the child with something which is harmful to development – can occur during pregnancy. The unborn child may not receive adequate nutrition, an example of prenatal neglect. He or she may be exposed to harmful substances, such as alcohol or drugs which cross freely from the mother's blood system to that of the child, an example of prenatal abuse.

The relationship between the child's parents during pregnancy may affect their subsequent bonding with the child. The kind of parenting that the parents themselves received strongly influences the expectations that they have for their child and for themselves as parents. Characteristics of the infant *in utero* come into play as well. Mothers sometimes note marked differences in their offspring even prior to birth. One may rarely move while another kicks and turns frequently. The characteristics of the child and the way the mother perceives them affects the developing bond.

Bonding at birth

Direct bonding between parents and child may begin during the very first moments of the child's life. Desmond found that during the first hour of life the normal infant is awake with eyes wide open.[10] Subsequently the infant usually falls into a deep sleep. The newborn infant, when held horizontally, reflexively turns toward the person holding them. Parents are pleased when the infant looks at them. In turn they will usually gently caress the child. Most parents of newborn babies use their first contact with the child to explore, to count fingers and toes, to see if the baby is physically normal.

This initial examination is part of the claiming process. After reassuring themselves, parents switch the focus of their exploration, identifying the ways that their infant is unique yet resembles other family members. During this process the parent is consciously and unconsciously looking for ways to tell this child from all others. Studies based on video-tapes of mother and child interactions made during deliveries and hospital stays indicate that when the mother does not take an active part in this claiming process, there is a high risk of severe mother–child difficulties in future months. However, it is not only adults who influence the development of the parent–child relationship; the infant, too, is a powerful factor. A child's physical disabilities will affect the parents just as surely as they will have an impact on the child. The child who is either under-responsive or very unsettled influences the parents' bonding to them. Medically fragile infants and those with physical disabilities are at greater risk of attachment problems than other babies. This is not because of maternal inadequacy but because high-risk infants' cueing and response capabilities are often unpredictable and atypical. Infants not only initiate interactions but actually shape mothering behaviours.[11]

The nervous system of a newborn infant is not well organised. Especially during the first month, the newborn child must make adjustments to life outside the womb. Sensitivity to internal and external stimuli is usually lower than it will be as he or she gets older. The newborn infant is irregular in many areas; he/she doesn't eat, sleep, or eliminate on schedule. The infant startles in response to a variety of stimuli; his/her movements seem jerky and unco-ordinated.

Throughout the first year of life and thereafter, the child's nervous system will become better organised. Interactions between the newborn child and its parents are a major force in this process. The influence of parent–child interactions on the child's developing nervous and hormonal systems may explain why some children who are not well attached have poor cognitive development and may be delayed in terms of physical development.

Interactions between parent and child involve all senses – touch, sound, sight, smell and taste. The child has the capacity to participate in these exchanges even in the first six months of life. However, children do not initially have control over their voluntary muscles. There is a natural order in which control is gained. In general, the child acquires muscle control from the head downward and from the central part of the body outward. Therefore, it is with the face muscles that the infant begins to participate actively in the attachment process.

The infant first learns to focus on objects eight or nine inches away, the distance between the infant's eyes and mother's face when nursing at the breast. From the age of four weeks, infants prefer looking at the human face to looking at other kinds of stimuli. By eight or nine weeks the infant is able to follow the movement of the human face and closely attend to it.

Face-to-face contact is important in developing connections with an infant. Spitz found that infants showed signs of pleasure even when they were presented with a mask of the human face.[12] Covering the lower part of the mask did not change their response. However, when the upper part of the mask was covered, even just one eye of it, the infants did not respond with pleasure. He speculated that the infant's response to human eyes may be innate rather than learned.

Between six weeks and eight months, the baby's smile becomes more and more selective.[13] By the time they are three to three-and-a-half months old, most infants demonstrate a preference for their own mother's face. Although infants at this age continue to show pleasure in response to others, reactions are more strongly and consistently evident in response to the mother. This preference for a specific face develops a full two months before the infant shows pleasure at the sight of a bottle or other object. Simultaneously, there is differential stopping of crying and increases in smiling and vocalisation in response to the mother's face.[14] From the time of birth, loud noises distress most infants and soft sounds quieten him or her. Infants respond preferentially to the higher pitched female voice. Wolff has demonstrated that infants turn towards sounds and that, from the time the child is three to four weeks old, he or she recognises the voice of the mother.[15] By the age of four weeks, the infant gurgles and coos in response to the human voice. Vocalisations increase when they are responded to. In fact, one of the functions of babbling seems to be to keep the adult close and to promote interaction between parent and child, thus facilitating attachment and bonding.

Body contact between parent and child also contributes to the attachment between them. In most societies infants are in more frequent body contact with their mothers than they are in western industrialised countries. The rhythmic movements that the child experiences as he or she is carried around by the mother are similar to those experienced before birth, and, as such, are likely to provide comfort and a sense of security. The rhythmic movement encourages growth in premature infants. Cradles and rocking chairs have long been used to help soothe irritable babies. In recent years an increasing number of parents have been using sling-like supports to permit closeness with their babies as they go about their daily housework and out on excursions. Some unsettled babies respond positively to this swaddling effect.

Overall, in these early months, infants respond most to the particular sensations that promote contact with other humans. They prefer looking at the human face and listening to the human voice. They prefer the feel of soft clothes and the sense of rhythmical movements experienced as their parent carries them. They prefer the taste of their mother's milk. MacFarlane showed that by five days of age the breast-fed infant could discriminate the smell of its mother's breastpad from others.[16]

Thus, infants are especially sensitive to developing attachment behaviours during the first six months of life. However, before sixteen weeks differential responses are fewer in number and less consistent. By sixteen to twenty-six weeks, the differential responses are more numerous and apparent. From six to seven months on, the preferential responses are plain for all to see in the majority of infants.

The infant's differential responses to primary carer

- 3–6 weeks: more vocal in response to carer
- 9 weeks: crying stops faster when held by carer
- 10 weeks: increased smiling in response to seeing carer

- 15 weeks: increased crying when carer departs from sight
- 18 weeks: watches carer when held by others
- 21 weeks: greets carer more warmly than others
- 22 weeks: explores more when in sight of carer
- 24 weeks: tries to follow carer when carer leaves

Attachment and bonding from six to twelve months

Between the age of six and nine months, the child learns to distinguish consistently between family members and strangers. The baby has developed an internalised early representation of family members, and begins to demonstrate fear or anxiety when approached by a stranger. The strength and frequency of these fear reactions increase as the child nears one year of age.

By the age of eight months, the child is playing a more active role in trying to keep adult carers close to him/her. The child obviously tries to catch the parent's attention, and increasing mobility makes it easier to achieve this aim. Attention-seeking activities on the part of the child are an important part of attachment building and should not be discouraged. By the age of nine to twelve months, child and primary carer will have developed a unique relationship in terms of who initiates interactions, how they are initiated, and how they are responded to. Often, one can virtually observe this delicate balance being achieved. Over the course of the first year, attachment between mother and child should increase, but dependency should decrease.

The infant's urge for closeness and attachment is so strong that, if the carer doesn't stay close, the child tries to draw the carer to him/her. When a parent rejects the child, clinging and whiny behaviour increases. In these cases, closeness to the parent is maintained with primarily negative rather than positive interactions. This has been described by Ainsworth as "anxious attachment" as opposed to the "secure attachment" which develops when the mother demonstrates that she is ready to remain close, thereby freeing the child's energies for other activities.

According to Ainsworth the anxious, insecure nine-to-twelve-month old may falsely appear more strongly attached to his/her mother than the secure child who can explore in a strange situation using mother as a secure base. The securely attached child may not be as distressed by the appearance of a stranger. The child will show awareness of the mother's absence, greet her on her return, and then resume previous activities.

In contrast, the insecure child is one who does not explore even when the mother is present. The child becomes extremely alarmed by the appearance of a stranger, seems helpless and in acute distress when mother leaves and, on her return, is either disinterested or in distress, but in either case is incapable of making an organised attempt to reach her. The child clings excessively. On the other hand, the avoidant child actively ignores the parent, turning or moving away, and does not look to the parent for comfort or stimulation.

Notes

1   Klaus M H and Kennell J H (1976) *Maternal-Infant Bonding*, St Louis: C V Mosby Company, US

2   Rutter M (1981) *Maternal Deprivation Reassessed*, London: Penguin Books

3   Goldstein J, Freud A and Solnit A J (1973) *Beyond the Best Interests of the Child*, New York: Macmillan Publishing, US

4   Bowlby J (1973) *Attachment and Loss, Volume 2, Separation: Anxiety and anger*, New York: Basic Books, US

5   Stroufe L A, Fox N E and Pancake V R (1983) 'Attachment and dependency in developmental perspective', *Child Development* 54, pp.1615–1627, US

6   Yogman M, 'Development of the father–infant relationship', Fitzgerald, Lester, Yogman (eds) *Theory and Research in Behavioral Paediatrics*, Vol 1, New York: Plenum Publishing Corporation, US

7   Bourguignon J P and Watson K W (1987) *After Adoption: A manual for professionals working with adoptive families*, Springfield Ill, Illinois Department of Children and Family Services, US

8   Winnicot D W (1958) *Collected Papers*, New York: Basic Books Inc, US

9   See 1 above

10   Desmond M M, Rudolph A J and Phitaksphraiwan P (1966) 'The Transitional Care Nursery: A mechanism of a preventative medicine', *Paediatric Clinics of North America*, 131, pp.651–658, US

11   Foley G M, *An Assessment Scale – Family attachment to the high risk infant*. A paper presented in May 1980 in Denver Co, US

12   Spitz R (1965) *The First Year of Life*, International Universities Press, New York, US

13   Fraiberg S (1977) *Every Child's Birthright: In defense of mothering*, Basic Books, New York, US

14   Ainsworth M D S (1967) *Infancy in Uganda, Infant Care and the Growth of Love*, Johns Hopkins University Press, Baltimore, US

15   Wolff P H (1966) *The Causes, Controls and Organization of Behavior in the Neonate*, International Universities Press, New York, US

16   MacFarlane J S (1975) In *Parent–Infant Interaction*, Ciba Foundation Symposium 33, Elsevier Publishing Co, Amsterdam, The Netherlands

Reproduced from *A Child's Journey through Placement* by Vera Fahlberg, published by BAAF in 1994, and which provides the knowledge base needed for working with children and families. © Vera Fahlberg

ON CHILDREN'S DEVELOPMENT

The following charts, by Mary Sheridan in *In Touch with Children*, BAAF, 1984, illustrate the developmental progress of infants and young children (0–33 months).

	Posture and large movements	**Vision and fine movements**
1 MONTH	● Lies back with head to one side; arm and leg on same side outstretched, or both arms flexed; knees apart, soles of feet turned inwards. ● Large jerky movements of limbs, arms more active than legs. ● At rest, hands closed and thumb turned in. ● Fingers and toes fan out during extensor movements of limbs. ● When cheek touched, turns to same side; ear gently rubbed, turns head away. ● When lifted or pulled to sit head falls loosely backwards. ● Held sitting, head falls forward, with back in one complete curve. ● Placed downwards on face, head immediately turns to side; arms and legs flexed under body, buttocks humped up. ● Held standing on hard surface, presses down feet, straightens body and often makes reflex "stepping" movements.	● Turns head and eyes towards light. ● Stares expressionlessly at brightness of window or blank wall. ● Follows pencil flash-lamp briefly with eyes at 1 foot. ● Shuts eyes tightly when pencil light shone directly into them at 1–2 inches. ● Notices silent dangling toy shaken in line of vision at 6–8 inches and follows its slow movement with eyes from side towards mid-line on level with face through approximately quarter circle, before head falls back to side. ● Gazes at mother's nearby face when she feeds or talks to him with increasingly alert facial expression.
3 MONTHS	● Now prefers to lie on back with head in mid-line. Limbs more pliable, movements smoother and more continuous. ● Waves arms symmetrically. Hands now loosely open. Brings hands together from side into mid-line over chest or chin. ● Kicks vigorously, legs alternating or occasionally together. ● Held sitting, holds back straight, except in lumbar region, with head erect and steady for several seconds before bobbing forwards. ● Placed downwards on face lifts head and upper chest well up in mid-line, using forearms as support, and often scratching at table surface; legs straight, buttocks flat. ● Held standing with feet on hard surface, sags at knees.	● Visually very alert, particularly interested in nearby human faces. ● Moves head deliberately to look around him. ● Follows adult's movements near cot. Follows dangling toy at 6–10 inches above face through half-circle from side to side, and usually also vertically from chest to brow. ● Watches movements of own hands before face and beginning to clasp and unclasp hands together in finger play. ● Recognises feeding bottle and makes eager welcoming movements as it approaches his face. ● Regards still objects within 6–10 inches for more than a second or two, but seldom fixates continuously. ● Comerges eyes as dangling toy is moved towards face. ● Defensive blink shown.
6 MONTHS	● Lying on back, raises head from pillow. ● Lifts legs into vertical and grasps foot. ● Sits with support in cot or pram and turns head from side to side to look around him. ● Moves arms in brisk and purposeful fashion and holds them up to be lifted. ● When hands grasped braces shoulders and pulls himself up. Kicks strongly, legs alternating. ● Can roll over, front to back. ● Held sitting, head is firmly erect, and back straight. May sit alone momentarily. ● Placed downwards on face lifts head and chest well up, supporting himself on extended arms. ● Held standing with feet touching hard surface bears weight on feet and bounces up and down actively.	● Visually insatiable: moves head and eyes eagerly in every direction. ● Eyes move in unison: squint now abnormal. ● Follows adult's movements across room. ● Immediately fixates interesting small objects within 6–12 inches (e.g., toy, bell, wooden cube, spoon, sweet) and stretches out both hands to grasp them. ● Uses whole hand in palmar grasp. ● When toys fall from hand over edge of cot forgets them. (Watches rolling balls of 2 to $^{1}/_{4}$ inch diameter at 10 feet.)

	Hearing and speech	**Social behaviour and play**
1 MONTH	● Startled by sudden loud noises, stiffens, quivers, blinks, screws eyes up, extends limbs, fans out fingers and toes, and may cry. ● Movements momentarily "frozen", when small bell rung gently 3–5 inches from ear for 3–5 seconds, with 5-second pauses: may "corner" eyes towards sound. ● Stops whimpering to sound of nearby soothing human voice, but not when screaming or feeding. ● Cries lustily when hungry or uncomfortable. ● Utters little guttural noises when content. ● Note – Deaf babies also cry and vocalise in this reflex way, but if very deaf do not usually show startle reflex to sudden noise. Blind babies may also move eyes towards a sound-making toy. Vision should always be checked separately.	● Sucks well. ● Sleeps much of the time when not being fed or handled. ● Expression still vague, but becoming more alert, progressing to social smiling about 5–6 weeks. ● Hands normally closed, but if opened, grasps examiner's finger when palm is touched. ● Stops crying when picked up and spoken to. ● Mother supports head when carrying, dressing and bathing.
3 MONTHS	● Sudden loud noises still distress, provoking blinking, screwing up of eyes, crying and turning away. ● Definite quietening or smiling to sound of mother's voice before she touches him, but not when screaming. ● Vocalises freely when spoken to or pleased. ● Cries when uncomfortable or annoyed. ● Quietens to tinkle of spoon in cup or to bell rung gently out of sight for 3–5 seconds at 6–12 inches from ear. ● May turn eyes and head towards sound: brows may wrinkle and eyes dilate. ● Often licks lips in response to sounds of preparation for feeding. ● Shows excitement at sound of approaching footsteps, running bath water, voices, etc. ● Note – Deaf baby, instead, may be obviously startled by another's sudden appearance beside cot.	● Fixes eyes unblinkingly on mother's face when feeding. ● Beginning to react to familiar situations – by smiles, coos, and excited movements showing that he recognises preparation for feeds, baths, etc. ● Responds with obvious pleasure to friendly handling, especially when accompanied by playful tickling and vocal sounds. ● Holds rattle for few moments when placed in hand, but seldom capable of regarding it at same time. ● Mother supports at shoulders when dressing and bathing.
6 MONTHS	● Turns immediately to mother's voice across room. ● Vocalises tunefully and often, using single and double syllables, e.g., ka, muh, goo, der, adah, er-leh. ● Laughs, chuckles and squeals aloud in play. ● Screams with annoyance. ● Shows evidence of response to different emotional tones of mother's voice. ● Responds to baby hearing tests at 1½ feet from each ear by correct visual localisation, but may show slightly brisker response on one side. (Tests employed – voice, rattle, cup and spoons, paper, bell: 2 seconds with 2-second pause.)	● Hands competent to reach for and grasp small toys. ● Most often uses a two-handed, scooping-in approach, but occasionally a single hand. ● Takes everything to mouth. ● Beginning to find feet interesting and even useful in grasping. ● Puts hands to bottle and pats it when feeding. ● Shakes rattle deliberately to make it sound, often regarding it closely at same time. ● Still friendly with strangers but occasionally shows some shyness or even slight anxiety, especially if mother is out of sight.

	Posture and large movements	**Vision and fine movements**
9 MONTHS	● Sits alone for 10–15 minutes on floor. ● Can turn body to look sideways while stretching out to grasp dangling toy or to pick up toy from floor. ● Arms and legs very active in cot, pram and bath. ● Progresses on floor by rolling or squirming. ● Attempts to crawl on all fours. ● Pulls self to stand with support. ● Can stand holding on to support for a few moments, but cannot lower himself. Held standing, steps purposefully on alternate feet.	● Very observant. ● Stretches out, one hand leading, to grasp small objects immediately on catching sight of them. ● Manipulates objects with lively interest, passing from hand to hand, turning over, etc. ● Pokes at small sweet with index finger. ● Grasps sweets, string, etc., between finger and thumb in scissor fashion. ● Can release toy by pressing against firm surface, but cannot yet put down precisely. ● Searches in correct place for toys dropped within reach of hands. ● Looks after toys falling over edge of pram or table. ● Watches activities of adults, children and animals within 10–12 feet with eager interest for several seconds at a time. (Watches rolling balls 2–⅛ inches at 10 feet.)
12 MONTHS	● Sits well and for indefinite time. ● Can rise to sitting position from lying down. ● Crawls rapidly, usually on all fours. ● Pulls to standing and lets himself down again holding on to furniture. ● Walks round furniture stepping sideways. ● Walks with one or both hands held. ● May stand alone for few moments. ● May walk alone.	● Picks up small objects, e.g. blocks, string, sweets and crumbs, with precise pincer grasp of thumb and index finger. ● Throws toys deliberately and watches them fall to ground. ● Looks in correct place for toys which roll out of sight. ● Points with index finger at objects he wants to handle or which interest him. ● Watches small toy pulled along floor across room 10 feet away. ● Out of doors watches movements of people, animals, motor cars, etc., with prolonged intent regard. ● Recognises familiars approaching from 20 feet or more away. ● Uses both hands freely, but may show preference for one. ● Clicks two bricks together in imitation. (Watches rolling balls 2–⅛ inches at 10 feet.)
15 MONTHS	● Walks unevenly with feet wide apart, arms slightly flexed and held above head or at shoulder level to balance. ● Starts alone, but frequently stopped by failing or bumping into furniture. ● Lets himself down from standing to sitting by collapsing backwards with bump, or occasionally by falling forward on hands and then back to sitting. ● Can get to feet alone. ● Crawls upstairs. ● Kneels unaided or with slight support on floor and in pram, cot and bath. ● May be able to stoop to pick up toys from floor.	● Picks up string, small sweets and crumbs neatly between thumb and finger. ● Builds tower of two cubes after demonstration. ● Grasps crayon and imitates scribble after demonstration. ● Looks with interest at pictures in book and pats page. ● Follows with eyes path of cube or small toy swept vigorously from table. ● Watches small toy pulled across floor up to 12 feet. ● Points imperiously to objects he wishes to be given. ● Stands at window and watches events outside intently for several minutes. (Watches and retrieves rolling balls of 2–⅛ inches at 10 feet.)

	Hearing and speech	**Social behaviour and play**
9 MONTHS	● Vocalises deliberately as means of interpersonal communication. ● Shouts to attract attention, listens, then shouts again. ● Babbles tunefully, repeating syllables in long strings (mam-mam, bab-bab, dad-dad, etc). ● Understands 'No-No' and 'Bye-Bye'. ● Tries to imitate adults' playful vocal sounds, e.g. smacking lips. cough, etc. (Immediate localising response to baby hearing tests at 3 feet from ear and above and below ear level.)	● Holds, bites and chews biscuits. ● Puts hands round bottle or cup when feeding. ● Tries to grasp spoon when being fed. ● Throws body back and stiffens in annoyance or resistance. ● Clearly distinguishes strangers from familiars, and requires reassurance before accepting their advances. ● Clings to known adult and hides face. ● Still takes everything to mouth. ● Seizes bell in one hand. ● Imitates ringing action, waving or banging it on table, pokes clapper or "drinks" from bowl. ● Plays peek-a-boo. ● Holds out toy held in hand to adult, but cannot yet give. ● Finds partially hidden toy. ● May find toy hidden under cup. ● Mother supports at lower spine when dressing.
12 MONTHS	● Knows and immediately turns to own name. ● Babbles loudly, tunefully and incessantly. ● Shows by suitable movements and behaviour that he understands several words in usual context (e.g. own and family names, walk, dinner, pussy, cup, spoon, ball, car). ● Comprehends simple commands associated with gesture (give it to daddy, come to mummy, say bye-bye, clap hands, etc). ● Imitates adults' playful vocalisations with gleeful enthusiasm. ● May hand examine common objects on request – spoon, cup, ball, shoe. (Immediate response to baby tests at 3–4$\frac{1}{2}$ feet but baby habituates.)	● Drinks from cup with little assistance. ● Chews. ● Holds spoon but usually cannot use it alone. ● Helps with dressing by holding out arm for sleeve and foot for shoe. ● Takes objects to mouth less often. ● Puts wooden cubes in and out of cup or box. ● Rattles spoon in cup in imitation. ● Seizes bell by handle and rings briskly in imitation, etc. ● Listens with obvious pleasure to percussion sounds. ● Repeats activities to reproduce effects. ● Gives toys to adult on request and sometimes spontaneously. ● Finds hidden toy quickly. ● Likes to be constantly within sight and hearing of adult. ● Demonstrates affection to familiars. ● Waves 'bye-bye' and claps hands in imitation or spontaneously. ● Child sits, or sometimes stands without support, while mother dresses.
15 MONTHS	● Jabbers loudly and freely, using wide range of inflections and phonetic units. ● Speaks 2–6 recognisable words and understands many more. ● Vocalises wishes and needs at table. ● Points to familiar persons, animals, toys, etc when requested. ● Understands and obeys simple commands (e.g. shut the door, give me the ball, get your shoes). (Baby test 4$\frac{1}{2}$–6 feet.)	● Holds cup when adult gives and takes back. ● Holds spoon, brings it to mouth and licks it, but cannot prevent its turning over. ● Chews well. ● Helps more constructively with dressing. ● Indicates when he has wet pants. ● Pushes large wheeled toy with handle on level ground. ● Seldom takes toys to mouth. ● Repeatedly casts objects to floor in play or rejection, usually without watching fall. ● Physically restless and intensely curious. ● Handles everything within reach. ● Emotionally labile. ● Closely dependent upon adult's reassuring presence. ● Needs constant supervision to protect child from dangers of extended exploration and exploitation of environment.

	Posture and large movements	**Vision and fine movements**
18 MONTHS	● Walks well with feet only slightly apart, starts and stops safely. ● Runs stiffly upright, eyes fixed on ground 1–2 yards ahead, but cannot continue to run round obstacles. ● Pushes and pulls large toys, boxes, etc., round floor. ● Can carry large doll or teddy-bear while walking and sometimes two. ● Backs into small chair or slides in sideways. ● Climbs forward into adult's chair then turns round and sits. ● Walks upstairs with helping hand. ● Creeps backwards downstairs. ● Occasionally bumps down a few steps on buttocks facing forwards. ● Picks up toy from floor without failing.	● Picks up small sweets, beads, pins, threads, etc, immediately on sight, with delicate pincer grasp. ● Spontaneous scribble when given crayon and paper, using preferred hand. ● Builds tower of three cubes after demonstration. ● Enjoys simple picture book, often recognising and putting finger on coloured items on page. ● Turns pages 2 or 3 at a time. ● Fixes eyes on small dangling toy up to 10 feet. (May tolerate this test with each eye separately.) ● Points to distant interesting objects out of doors. (Watches and retrieves rolling balls 2–1/8 inches at 10 feet.) (Possibly recognises special miniature toys at 10 feet.)
21 MONTHS	● Runs safely on whole foot, stopping and starting with ease and avoiding obstacles. ● Squats to rest or to play with object on ground and rises to feet without using hands. ● Walks backwards pulling large toy. ● Pulls wheeled toy by cord. ● Climbs on furniture to look out of window or open doors, etc, and can get down again. ● Walks upstairs and down holding on to rail or wall: two feet to a step. ● Throws small ball without falling. ● Walks into large ball when trying to kick it. ● Sits astride large wheeled toy and propels forward with feet on ground.	● Picks up pins and thread, etc., neatly and quickly. Removes paper wrapping from small sweet. ● Builds tower of six cubes (or 6 +). ● Spontaneous circular scribble and dots when given paper and pencil. ● Imitates vertical line (and sometimes V). ● Enjoys picture books, recognising fine details in favourite pictures. ● Turns pages singly. ● Recognises familiar adults in photograph after once shown. ● Hand preference becoming evident. (Immediately catches sight of and names special miniature toys at 10 feet distance. Will now usually tolerate this test with each eye separately.) (Watches and retrieves rolling balls 2–1/8 inches at 10 feet.)
24 MONTHS	● Walks upstairs alone but downstairs holding rail, two feet to a step. ● Runs well straight forward and climbs easy nursery apparatus. ● Pushes and pulls large toys skilfully, but has difficulty in steering them round obstacles. ● Jumps with two feet together. ● Can stand on tiptoe if shown. ● Kicks large ball. ● Sits on tricycle and steers with hands, but still usually propels with feet on ground.	● Picks up pins, threads, etc, with each eye covered separately. ● Builds tower of seven (or 7 +) cubes and lines blocks to form "train". ● Recognises minute details in picture books. ● Imitates horizontal line and circle (also usually T and V). ● Paints strokes, dots and circular shapes on easel. ● Recognises himself in photographs when once shown. ● Recognises miniature toys and retrieves balls 2–1/8 inches at 10 feet, each eye separately. (May also match special single letter-cards V, 0, T, H at 10 feet.)

	Hearing and speech	**Social behaviour and play**
18 MONTHS	● Continues to jabber tunefully to himself at play. ● Uses 6–20 recognisable words and understands many more. ● Echoes prominent or last word addressed to him. ● Demands desired objects by pointing accompanied by loud, urgent vocalisation or single words. ● Enjoys nursery rhymes and tries to join in. ● Attempts to sing. ● Shows his own or doll's hair, shoe, nose. (Possibly special 5 toy test. Possibly 4 animals picture test.)	● Lifts and holds cup between both hands. ● Drinks without spilling. ● Hands cup back to adult. ● Chews well. ● Holds spoon and gets food to mouth. ● Takes off shoes, socks, hat. ● Indicates toilet needs by restlessness and vocalisation. ● Bowel control usually attained. ● Explores environment energetically. ● No longer takes toys to mouth. ● Remembers where objects belong. ● Casts objects to floor in play or anger less often. ● Briefly imitates simple activities, e.g. reading book, kissing doll, brushing floor. ● Plays contentedly alone, but likes to be near adult. ● Emotionally still very dependent upon familiar adult, especially mother. ● Alternates between clinging and resistance.
21 MONTHS	● Uses 50 or more recognisable words and understands many more. ● Puts two or more words together to form simple sentences. ● Refers to himself by name. ● Talks to himself continually as he plays. ● Echolalia almost constant, with one or more stressed words repeated. ● Constantly asking names of objects. ● Joins in nursery rhymes and songs. ● Shows correctly and repeats words for hair, hand, feet, nose, eyes, mouth, shoe on request. (6 toy test, 4 animals picture test.)	● Lifts and drinks from cup and replaces on table. ● Spoon-feeds without spilling. ● Asks for food and drink. ● Chews competently. ● Puts on hat and shoes. ● Verbalises toilet needs in reasonable time. ● Dry during day. ● Turns door handles. ● Often runs outside to explore. ● Follows mother round house and copies domestic activities in simultaneous play. ● Engages in simple make-believe activities. ● Constantly demanding mother's attention. ● Clings tightly in affection, fatigue or fear. ● Tantrums when frustrated but attention readily distracted. ● Defends own possessions with determination. ● As yet no idea of sharing. ● Plays near other children but not with them. ● Resentful of attention shown to other children.
24 MONTHS	● Uses 200 or more recognisable words but speech shows numerous infantilisms. ● Knows full name. ● Talks intelligibly to himself at play concerning events happening here and now. ● Echolalia persists. ● Continually asking questions beginning 'What?', 'Where?' ● Uses pronouns, I, me and you. ● Stuttering in eagerness common. ● Says a few nursery rhymes. ● Enjoys simple familiar stories read from picture book. (6 toy test, 4 animals picture test, 1st cube test. Full doll vocabulary.)	● Eats skilfully with spoon and may use fork. ● Pulls down pants or knickers at toilet, but seldom able to replace. ● Dry through night if lifted. ● Very active, restless and rebellious. ● Throws violent tantrums when thwarted or unable to express urgent needs and less easily distracted. ● Emotionally still very dependent upon adults. ● Prolonged domestic make-believe play (putting dolls to bed, washing clothes, driving motor cars, etc.) but with frequent reference to friendly adult. ● Watches other children at play interestedly and occasionally joins in for a few minutes, but little notion of sharing playthings or adult's attention.

	Posture and large movements	**Vision and fine movements**
27 MONTHS	● Walks alone upstairs with alternating feet and downstairs with two feet to step. ● Usually jumps from bottom step. ● Climbs nursery apparatus with agility. ● Can turn round obstacles and corners while running and also while pushing and pulling large toys. ● Rides tricycle and can turn wide corners on it. ● Can walk on tiptoe. ● Stands momentarily on one foot when shown. ● Sits with feet crossed at ankles.	● Picks up pins, threads, etc., with each eye covered separately. ● Builds tower of nine cubes, also ($3^1/2$) bridge of three from model. ● Can close fist and wiggle thumb in imitation. R and L. ● Copies circle (also V, H, T). ● Imitates cross. ● Draws man with head and usually indication of features or one other part. ● Matches two or three primary colours (usually red and yellow correct, but may confuse blue and green). ● Paints "pictures" with large brush on easel. ● Cuts with scissors. (Recognises special miniature toys at 10 feet. Performs single-letter vision test at 10 feet. Five letters.)
30 MONTHS	● Turns sharp corners running, pushing and pulling. ● Walks alone up and downstairs, one foot per step. ● Climbs ladders and trees. ● Can run on tiptoe. ● Expert rider of tricycle. ● Hops on one foot. ● Stands on one foot 3–5 seconds. ● Arranges or picks up objects from floor by bending from waist with knees extended.	● Picks up pins, thread, crumbs, etc., with each eye covered separately. ● Builds tower of 10 or more cubes and several "bridges" of three on request. ● Builds three steps with six cubes after demonstration. ● Imitates spreading of hand and bringing thumb into opposition with each finger in turn. R and L. ● Copies cross (also V, H, T, O). ● Draws man with head, legs, features, trunk, and (often) arms. ● Draws very simple house. ● Matches and names four primary colours correctly. (Single-letter vision test at 10 feet, seven letters: also near chart to bottom.)
33 MONTHS	● Runs lightly on toes. ● Active and skilful in climbing, sliding. swinging, digging and various "stunts". ● Skips on alternate feet. ● Dances to music. ● Can stand on one foot 8–10 seconds. ● Can hop 2–3 yards forwards on each foot separately. ● Grips strongly with either hand.	● Picks up minute objects when each eye is covered separately. ● Builds three steps with six cubes from model. ● Copies square and triangle (also letters: V, T, H, O, X, L, A, C, U, Y). ● Writes a few letters spontaneously. ● Draws recognisable man with head, trunk, legs, arms and features. ● Draws simple house with door, windows, roof and chimney. ● Counts fingers on one hand with index finger of other. ● Names four primary colours and matches 10 or 12 colours. (Full nine-letter vision chart at 20 feet and near test to bottom.)

	Hearing and speech	**Social behaviour and play**
27 MONTHS	Large intelligible vocabulary but speech still shows many infantile phonetic substitutions. Gives full name and sex, and (sometimes) age. Uses plurals and pronouns. Still talks to himself in long monologues mostly concerned with the immediate present, including make-believe activities. Carries on simple conversations, and verbalises past experiences. Asks many questions beginning 'What?', 'Where?', 'Who?' Listens eagerly to stories and demands favourites over and over again. Knows several nursery rhymes. (7 toy test, 4 animals picture test. lst or 2nd cube test, 6 "high frequency" word pictures.)	Eats with fork and spoon. Washes hands, but needs supervision in drying. Can pull pants and knickers down and up, but needs help with buttons. Dry through night. General behaviour more amenable. Affectionate and confiding. Likes to help with adult's activities in house and garden. Makes effort to keep his surroundings tidy. Vividly realised make-believe play including invented people and objects. Enjoys floor play with bricks, boxes, toy trains and cars, alone or with siblings. Joins in play with other children in and outdoors. Understands sharing playthings, sweets, etc. Shows affection for younger siblings. Shows some appreciation of past and present.
30 MONTHS	Speech completely intelligible. Shows only a few infantile substitutions usually k/t/th/f/s and r/l/ w/y groups. Gives connected account of recent events and experiences. Gives name, sex, home address and (usually) age. Eternally asking questions 'Why?', 'When?', 'How?' and meanings of words. Listens to and tells long stories sometimes confusing fact and fantasy. (7 toy test, 1st picture vocabulary test, 2nd cube test. 6 "high frequency" word pictures.)	Eats skilfully with spoon and fork. Washes and dries hands. Brushes teeth. Can undress and dress except for back buttons, laces and ties. General behaviour markedly self-willed. Inclined to verbal impertinence when wishes crossed but can be affectionate and compliant. Strongly dramatic play and dressing-up favoured. Constructive out-of-doors building with any large material to hand. Needs other children to play with and is alternately co-operative and aggressive with them as with adults. Understands taking turns. Shows concern for younger siblings and sympathy for playmates in distress. Appreciates past, present and future.
33 MONTHS	Speech fluent and grammatical. Articulation correct except for residual confusions of s/f/th and r/l/w/y groups. Loves stories and acts them out in detail later. Gives full name, age and home address. Gives age and (usually) birthday. Defines concrete nouns by use. Asks meaning of abstract words. (2 "high frequency" picture vocabulary or word lists. 3rd cube test, 6 sentences.)	Uses knife and fork. Washes and dries face and hands, but needs help and supervision for rest. Undresses and dresses alone. General behaviour more sensible, controlled and responsibly independent. Domestic and dramatic play continued from day to day. Plans and builds constructively. Floor games very complicated. Chooses own friends. Co-operative with companions and understands need for rules and fair play. Appreciates meaning of clocktime in relation to daily programme. Tender and protective towards younger children and pets. Comforts playmates in distress.

ON ATTACHMENT FORMATION

Attachment and resilience concepts

Secure Base is founded on attachment theory. An in-depth knowledge of attachment theory and research is not essential for practitioners or caregivers to use the model, but an understanding of some of the basic concepts of attachment is helpful. Here we provide brief summaries of the attachment concepts that are particularly relevant to the model, including the link between attachment and resilience.

- Attachment formation
- Secure base
- Internal working models
- Mind-mindedness
- Attachment and resilience
- Impact of abuse and neglect
- Secure and insecure attachment patterns
- The importance of a secure base

Attachment formation

The starting point of John Bowlby's theory of attachment is an evolutionary one, in that babies are seen as having a biological drive to *seek proximity* to an adult, usually the primary caregiver or caregivers, in order to survive danger (1969, 1973, 1980). The goal for the infant of this drive for closeness is to feel safe, secure and protected. This leads to a range of proximity-promoting *attachment behaviours*.

Attachment behaviours may attract the caregiver's attention in a positive way, for example, cooing, smiling and reaching out. But attachment behaviours will include protest behaviours, such as crying and fretting, which will also bring the caregiver closer in order to soothe the child and end the behaviour. In the toddler years, attachment behaviours will include more direct actions, such as approaching, following, clinging and other behavioural strategies that can achieve proximity to the attachment figure.

All of these attachment behaviours give strong signals that should lead caregivers to respond to the needs of the baby or the older child. In the first months of life, the signals from the baby are repeated and need to be responded to countless times each day. When the baby is hungry, lonely or uncomfortable, the sensitive and responsive caregiver will both recognise and react promptly to meet the baby's needs. This experience of having needs recognised and met provides a secure base that settles the baby and reduces his anxiety, which, in turn, allows him to play and explore. When the baby is relaxed, smiling and playful, the caregiver will also share and reinforce this mood. Through the process of attachment behaviours being responded to promptly and appropriately, the baby's survival is ensured, and his emotional, social and physical development is enhanced and maximised in the context of the relationship. Recent research has shown that sensitive caregiving is also necessary to promote healthy brain development in the first two years of life (Howe, 2011).

As attachment behaviours become more organised and demands for food or play become more targeted, the adults who respond to them become highly significant to the growing baby. In optimal conditions, attachment behaviours become linked with strong feelings of joy and delight in both the child and the caregiver. Caregivers, of course, respond to the needs and demands of their children in different ways and this gives rise to the different secure and insecure attachment patterns discussed below.

Selective attachments, then, begin to form from birth. Early infancy is a particularly sensitive period for the development of attachments, but there are further opportunities throughout childhood. During the toddler years, where there has been continuity of sensitive care, mobility, play and language develop, providing opportunities to extend attachment relationships to other close adults. Children of this age, who have not experienced sensitive care and move to a new foster or adoptive family, can develop secure attachments to new caregivers if the caregivers provide sensitive care.

By the age of three or four, another shift occurs as secure children become able to think about their own and other people's thoughts and feelings – which is key to their ability to manage relationships not only with adults but also with peers.

During the pre-school and primary years, secure children develop the capacity to hold the selective secure base relationships in mind when they are separated from family caregivers (for example, at nursery or school), leaving them free to explore and learn, but also able to turn to other trusted adults for support if needed. Also during this stage, children who are experiencing sensitive parenting continue to learn to manage their feelings, co-operate with others and take into account the thoughts and feelings of others in more complex ways.

During adolescence, secure young people are becoming increasingly confident and competent. Their thinking is more complex and more reflective and they can anticipate the future. There may be experimentation with the rejection of parental norms and values and moving away from the secure base, but family ties, parental pleasure in their successes, and the knowledge that the secure base is still available in times of difficulty remain very important.

The formation and development of attachment relationships continue through the lifespan, so that adult children's relationships with their parents will change, and in romantic attachment relationships we both care for and receive care from our partners – becoming both care seekers and caregivers. The transition to parenthood requires a mature transformation into a caregiver who can provide a secure base for a child, although parents still need support from their own secure base in partners, adult relatives or friends.

A secure base

A secure base is provided through a relationship with one or more sensitive and responsive attachment figures who meet the child's needs and to whom the child can turn as a safe haven, when upset or anxious (Bowlby, 1988). When children develop trust in the availability and reliability of this relationship, their anxiety is reduced and they can therefore explore and enjoy their world, safe in the knowledge that they can return to their secure base for help if needed.

The concept of a secure base is essential to our understanding of relationship formation and children's development. It links attachment and exploration, and provides the basis of a secure attachment. A securely attached child does not only seek comfort from an attachment figure, but by feeling safe to explore, develops confidence, competence and resilience.

Internal working models

To understand the lessons that children learn in early relationships and why they go on to affect subsequent relationships, Bowlby developed the concept of "internal working models". An internal working model is a set of expectations and beliefs about the self, about others and about relationships. Thus, the internal working model of an individual will contain particular expectations and beliefs:

- Am I loveable and worthy of love?
- Are other people available, interested and able to help/protect/support me?

Internal working models begin to form in early infancy. If, for example, the baby finds that his feelings of hunger and his accompanying crying behaviour result in a prompt response from a loving adult who makes him feel better, he will learn that certain of his behaviours are linked with the positive behaviours of his caregiver. At the same time, he will feel that he is loved and nurtured and that he "deserves" this response. A more generalised expectation of adults as people who are likely to be there to help and protect also develops over time. At the other end of the spectrum, a parental response that is unavailable or cold will lead to an internal working model of the attachment figure as rejecting, the self as unworthy of care, and others as not to be relied on for help and support.

The models are termed "working" models because they are subject to change and development according to changing experiences in relationships. Bowlby observed that these models are established in the first few years of life, and as children get older, models retain some flexibility but do become increasingly resistant to change. This means that foster care and adoption need to provide family environments that are able to stick with troubled children who take time to learn to trust. But if families can offer this, then children's working models can change in a positive direction right through adolescence.

Children's behaviours become organised around their expectations of themselves and others and, as they grow older, these expectations tend to influence the way in which others relate to them. In this way, positive and negative cycles of reinforcement are set up. For example, the child who feels good about himself and expects others to be mostly warm and friendly will present himself to a potential friendship group in a way that signals 'You can trust me. I will be a good friend', and so elicits a positive response. Conversely, a child who expects rejection, has low self-esteem and a sense of the world as a hostile place is likely to signal defiantly 'I don't need or want your friendship, don't come close to me', which tends to bring about further rejection of the kind the child most fears. Positive internal working models can cope with a degree of rejection. Negative internal working models tend to see hostility even in neutral behaviour. Thus to change children's negative expectations of self and others requires caregivers who can sustain availability and sensitive responding in the face of apparent hostility and lack of trust.

Mind-mindedness

Bowlby's view of what was necessary for sensitive care relied on the caregiver thinking about the thoughts and feelings of the child, and over time enabling the child to think about their own thoughts and feelings and the thoughts and feelings of the caregiver and other adults and children. This builds into an ability to make connections between feelings and behaviour in self and others – the capacity to mentalise. This ability in the child is strongly related to resilience, as it is only when a child is able to mentalise that they are able to make sense of themselves, their experiences and their relationships and be able to face new experiences and relationships with confidence.

Modern attachment researchers have built on the foundations of Bowlby's thinking. Elizabeth Meins and her colleagues have shown the importance for secure attachment and social development of what she calls the caregiver's "mind-mindedness" – the capacity to be interested in what the child is thinking and feeling, to see things from the *child's point of view*, and to *communicate this to the child* (Meins *et al*, 2003).

This process begins in infancy, with the sensitive caregiver viewing even the tiny baby as having thoughts and feelings that need to be understood. The caregiver speculates about these thoughts and feelings and reflects them back to the baby ('Are you hungry?' 'Were you feeling lonely?'). In doing so, the baby begins to understand and make sense of his inner experiences and feelings and gradually to manage and express them appropriately. As the baby grows, the mind-minded caregiver also finds it natural to talk to the baby about their own feelings and behaviour ('Mummy's tired now, so we'll stop the game and have a drink') and that of others ('Your friend felt sad when you wouldn't share the toy, that's why she went off into the other room'). Through this sort of interaction and verbalisation of thoughts and feelings, the child learns to distinguish between different feelings in self and others, to express feelings in ways that are effective and socially acceptable, and to empathise with others.

David Howe (2011, p. 29) suggests: 'Parents who focus on their children's subjective experiences help them understand their own and other people's psychological states and how these are linked to actions and behaviour.' This builds the child's capacity to mentalise, to understand the links betweenmental states and behaviour.

Attachment and resilience

Many of the qualities that we associate with sensitive caregiving and secure attachment, and which are central to Secure Base, have strong links to the theory of resilience.

For a child, becoming resilient means developing the capacity not only to overcome past adversities, but to face future challenges with hope, confidence and competence. This may mean facing the ordinary challenges of starting a new school or not being picked for the football team. For adopted and fostered children, it may include facing more complex cognitive and emotional tasks, such as managing contact with birth relatives or coming to terms with a troubling life story.

Factors that are linked to resilience, such as trust in other people for support, positive self-esteem, self-efficacy and the capacity to reflect on your feelings and the feelings of others, are also associated with security of attachment. It is important to note that resilience, like a sense of security, can be promoted by the quality of caregiving a child receives.

The impact of abuse and neglect

Because most children who are fostered or adopted from care have experienced harmful parenting, it is important for caregivers to understand the impact of abuse and neglect on children's thinking, behaviour and development.

Where infants and children have not experienced the kind of sensitive parenting that promotes security and resilience – and instead have experienced parenting that was a source of fear – they will find it difficult to trust and will struggle to manage their feelings and behaviour. They are therefore likely to react negatively to offers of care and concern from foster carers and adoptive parents and may recreate in their new families cycles of negative behaviour that lead to them being rejected again (Crittenden, 1995).

Children have adopted behaviours that helped them to survive when anxious and afraid, but these strategies bring additional difficulties in new families, which need to be managed with sensitivity and patience.

Secure and insecure attachment patterns

Attachment patterns are ways of thinking and behavioural strategies that children develop in order to feel safe and to maximise their opportunities for receiving protection and care from significant adults.

Different attachment patterns emerge in response to different types of caregiving. Ainsworth (1971) used a combination of home-based observations of caregiving in infancy and a laboratory situation called the Strange Situation to identify secure and two insecure (avoidant and ambivalent) attachment patterns. The Strange Situation involves the infant (12–18 months old) experiencing a series of brief separations and reunions with a primary caregiver while their reactions are observed, recorded and then analysed. Later research by Main and Solomon (1986) into those cases where the infant's recorded behaviour could not be explained using the existing three patterns, identified a third insecure attachment pattern – disorganised attachment. Below, each of these four patterns is described in relation to the caregiving approach associated with it.

Secure attachment patterns

Secure attachment occurs when the infant or child is cared for by available, sensitive and responsive caregivers, who are accepting and co-operative, promoting trust and competence. When this care is predictable and mind-minded, the child over time becomes able to think about and manage thoughts, feelings and behaviour in order to become competent and successful in activities and relationships outside the family. In later adolescence and adulthood, this pattern is referred to as *autonomous* or *free to evaluate*, because of the importance of being able to think and to regulate emotions before acting.

Avoidant attachment patterns

When the caregiver finds it difficult to accept or respond sensitively to the infant's needs, the infant may find that their demands are rejected, and their feelings minimised and that the caregiver tries to take over in an intrusive, insensitive way. Although the rejecting caregiver's overall role in providing practical care and protection continues, the infant learns to shut down on their feelings in order to avoid upsetting the caregiver and provoking rejection or intrusion. It is safer and more comfortable to be self-reliant and undemanding and this also makes it more likely that the caregiver will stay close. The child is not avoiding a relationship, but avoiding showing feelings, particularly negative feelings, in order to maintain some kind of proximity and relationship. In later adolescence and adulthood, this pattern of minimising and defensively devaluing feelings and the significance of relationships is referred to as *dismissing*. As in infancy, the need for closeness and relationships continues but cannot be appropriately expressed or managed.

Ambivalent attachment patterns

In contrast, where the caregiver responds to the infant's demands, but only in a sporadic and unpredictable way that is insensitive to the child's signals, the infant finds it difficult to achieve proximity in a reliable way. Care and protection are sometimes available, but the caregiving is *uncertain* and ineffective. Initially, the infant may simply make demands almost constantly to attract and keep the attention of the caregiver or may become rather helpless in the absence of a predictably successful strategy. Over time, the infant tends to become needy and angry, a "clingy" but distrustful and *resistant* child. In later adolescence and adulthood, this pattern is referred to as *preoccupied* and *enmeshed,* but preoccupation with relationships and the need to be loved can be observed even in very young children who lack trust.

Disorganised attachment patterns

Where the caregiver is rejecting, unpredictable *and* frightening or frightened, the infant is caught in a dilemma of 'fear without solution' (Main and Hesse, 1990). Caregivers abdicate the caregiving role, experiencing themselves as out of control and become *hostile/helpless* to protect the child. The infant's drive to approach the caregiver for care and protection results in fear and increased rather than decreased anxiety. The absence of a possible strategy to achieve comfortable proximity in infancy leads to confused and disorganised behaviours. But over time the pre-school child starts to develop controlling behaviours to enable them to feel some degree of predictability and safety. These controlling behaviours usually include role-reversal in which a child acts towards others like a parent might towards a child, e.g. punitively aggressive, compulsively caregiving or compulsively self-reliant, i.e. not accepting care. However, feelings of anxiety and fear remain unresolved and reappear in sometimes chaotic and destructive forms at times of stress. In later adolescence and adulthood, this pattern is referred to as *unresolved,* reflecting the fact that experiences of loss, trauma or fear continue to trouble the adult mind.

Although many children who have been maltreated are likely to have disorganised patterns of attachment, not all children who are disorganised will have been maltreated. A caregiver may have experienced unresolved loss and trauma in the past. This may make the parent a source of anxiety rather than comfort for the infant, but does not mean that the parent is necessarily neglectful or abusive. However, the child may develop difficulties in their capacity to manage their emotions, their relationships and their behaviour.

The importance of a secure base

What happens when children do not have a secure base?

Early experiences of separation or neglectful or abusive parenting will cause children to remain anxious and to distrust close relationships. Children adapt to the lack of a secure base by developing different patterns of behaviour. For instance, they may become wary and defended (avoidant) or especially needy and demanding of care and attention (ambivalent). Children who have experienced unpredictable or frightening care may try to make their environment more predictable through role-reversing and controlling behaviour (disorganised). These behaviours are characteristic of insecure attachment patterns and indicate an absence of a secure base.

What happens when children are removed from a harmful family environment?

For many children, serious experiences of neglect and maltreatment will have had a profound effect. They will have developed negative expectations of adults and themselves as part of their internal working model of relationships. They will transfer these expectations into new environments (such as foster or adoptive families), along with the patterns of defensive behaviour that have functioned as survival strategies in the past. In these circumstances, children will find it hard to let adults come close enough to establish trusting relationships and provide a secure base. The risk, then, is that feelings and behaviours might become fixed in destructive cycles and the damage of the past will not be healed.

What can be done to help?

Attachment theory would suggest that exposure to warm, consistent and reliable caregiving can change children's previous expectations, both of close adults and of themselves and there is ample evidence from research and practice to support this (Wilson *et al*, 2003; Beek and Schofield, 2004; Cairns, 2004; Schofield and Beek, 2009; Howe, 2011).

The role of adults who can provide secure base caregiving, therefore, is of central importance. They must take on a parenting/caregiving role for the child, but they must also become a *therapeutic* caregiver in order to change the child's most fundamental sense of self and others (internal working model).

In order to achieve this, they must care for the child in ways that demonstrate, implicitly and explicitly, to the child that they are trustworthy and reliable, physically and emotionally available and sensitive to his needs. In addition, they must be mindful of the protective strategies that the child has learned in order to feel safe in the past and adjust their approaches so that their parenting feels comfortable and acceptable to the child rather than undermining or threatening.

The ensuing relationships will provide a secure base, from which children can develop and be supported to explore and maximise their potential. Achieving this outcome is the goal of the Secure Base model.

What may be the impact on caregivers of providing a secure base to troubled children?

There is no doubt that although offering therapeutic care that changes how troubled children feel about themselves and relate to other people is very rewarding, it is also a very emotionally demanding role. Children who have had to survive frightening environments in the past may have adopted behaviours that can alarm and overwhelm caregivers. Foster and adoptive caregivers need support from their own networks and from professionals to be able to maintain their patience, sensitivity and commitment to the child, even in the face of initial anger and rejection by the child.

Do adults/caregivers also need a secure base?

Yes. As we move through the lifespan, we form new attachment relationships with friends and partners. These relationships serve the same function for adults as they do for children: they provide a secure base that offers comfort and reassurance and, at the same time, allows us to operate in the world with confidence. In the words of Bowlby:

All of us, from the cradle to the grave, are happiest when life is organised as a series of excursions, long or short, from the secure base provided by our attachment figures.

(Bowlby, 1988, p. 62)

Reproduced from *Promoting Attachment and Resilience*, by Gillian Schofield and Mary Beek, published by BAAF in 2014 (pp 4–12). This guide offers a model of caregiving – Secure Base – that is based on theories of attachment and resilience. © Gill Schofield and Mary Beek

Becoming mummy

Hearing me being called mummy was at first quite a laugh for my friends, I think. I was aware of nudges and giggles each time Alan said it.

Me: Come on, be honest, it was weird hearing Alan call me mummy, wasn't it?

Annie: Well, it was a bit. It just took a little getting used to, that's all. We soon did get used to it.

Me: It took me a while, actually.

Annie: I know. I suppose I'd been a mummy for quite some time already before my children actually were able to say mummy. It was nice, though. I liked hearing Alan call you mummy.

For my parents, I think hearing Alan call me mummy was very moving, but of course they were also grappling with being Grandma and Grandad for the first time!

Several months after Alan came to live with me, I took him to London and we visited my old office. It was much more of a shock to my former work colleagues, I think, to see me in this unfamiliar role, particularly for those of them who hadn't quite believed I would go through with it. They thought Alan was adorable, naturally, but it was as if I had grown horns or changed colour or something. I had by then become accustomed to being a mummy, and all that it entailed, but they found it hard to see what I had already realised, which is that I hadn't actually changed at all. I was still me – same sense of humour, same personality – but now I had a little extra something – Alan – who had become the centre of my universe, and work just wasn't that interesting to me any more.

My new friends, the ones I met through toddler groups and pre-school, just accepted I was a mum because they hadn't known me in any other context. My old close friends soon got used to it. Even I got used to being a mummy much more quickly than I had imagined. For Alan, though, it was a slightly more complicated process. Alan knew that I was Mummy – that was my name – but although he knew other children had mummies he didn't really know what a mummy was for. For many months after Alan first came to live with me, I really had the impression that he didn't understand that we belonged together in a family unit. If we were out with other adults, even in an environment where he didn't know anyone else, I would often get the distinct feeling that he would have been happy to go home with anyone who asked him. He was happy to accept attention and hugs from any adult prepared to give them, particularly men. It worried me enormously, because Alan had absolutely no fear or reticence with adult strangers. Even now, several years later, I sometimes have to talk to him about being familiar with adults that he doesn't know. It would take months before I really felt, when we were out and about, that Alan knew he was supposed to be with me, and that he had to come home with me, and that he was happy about it.

In time, clues to Alan's attachment to me started to appear – for instance, if I ever left him with anyone, which wasn't often, he would start to ask where I was after a certain amount of time. Having been very compliant in his first few months with me, he started to be rather naughty and angry with me, which I took to be a sign that he felt secure enough to risk upsetting me. If he fell and hurt himself, instead of trying hard not to show that he was hurt, he would cry and come and find me. I had always tried to be affectionate and physically close to him, which helped the bonding process enormously. We hugged a lot – we still do. He is a very cuddly child.

Reproduced from *Flying Solo*, by Julia Wise, published by BAAF in 2007 (pp 52–54). In this personal narrative, the author describes adopting as a single parent, and her life with Alan, her adopted son. © Julia Wise

ON DEALING WITH LOSS AND GRIEF

Separation and loss are major themes in the lives of children adopted and in foster care, whether it is the infant separated from a mother at birth or the older child who has experienced separation from birth parents and siblings plus a number of moves within the care system. Children require time to grieve and to pass through the different stages of grief just like any adult who has experienced a bereavement. Children's grieving process can take years, and the difficulty for some children is not having the space to grieve, their energies often being focused on survival. Adults often expect children to be able to adjust to major changes in their lives without due recognition of the impact. Children who are unable to grieve may become "stuck" developmentally, unable to move beyond the stage of anger, denial or despair. Much of their emotional energy is taken up with the pain associated with their loss and there is little left over for growth or movement. Children may close down emotionally and, because their development is "stuck", they may function below their chronological age emotionally, cognitively and behaviourally. As we know, children are more likely to communicate their feelings through behaviour. Grief may be expressed through acting out, anger and aggression, but it can also manifest itself through withdrawal and depression.

Applicants need to understand the significance of loss in children's lives and be sensitive to their moods and behaviour...Sensitivity to major events such as birthdays and Christmas or other festive occasions, the changing of the seasons, the start of a school term, anything that serves as a poignant reminder to the child of their loss, will help later on when, as new parents, they see a sudden, seemingly unexpected, change of mood or behaviour in their child. Understanding the need for appropriate regression, and thinking about how they will teach or model a range of feelings, will be important.

Reproduced from *Making Good Assessments* by Pat Beesley, published by BAAF in 2010 (pp 168–169). © BAAF

Grief

When the guinea pig died, we put her gently in a shoe box and covered her with flowers. We chose a spot in the garden under a rose bush, and dug a hole for her grave. She was laid to rest there, and we remembered what joy she had brought us in her long (for a guinea pig) life of gentleness and affection, her funny little ways, and how she helped to bring up Charlie the duckling when his mother was taken by the fox. We put a heavy stone over the grave, for we wanted her to return to the elements in her own sweet time. The fox should not have her.

'I remember a baby boy. My mum bathed him and the water was too hot and he cried and cried. Then he stopped crying, and he was still, and my mum put him in the airing cupboard. After that I got taken away.'

'When my mum died, I was in a foster home. Two people came to see me, and they talked at me for about half an hour. I didn't know what they were on about. Then one of them said, 'I'm sorry, but your mum's dead.' And the other one said, 'Do you want to go to the funeral?' I said 'No, thank you,' and they went away.

At the age of eight, Tim became ill. Viral meningitis as a complication of mumps. Soaring fever and obviously excruciating pain. Rushed to hospital for tests, the good news being that it was viral and not life-threatening, the bad news that it must run its painful course, with no help for it but some relief of pain and endless patient sitting by the bedside providing soothing washes, and sips of fluid to prevent Tim dehydrating. We brought him home and put him to bed, and everyone did their bit of being sympathetic and moving around as quietly as usually boisterous children can remember to be. They offered games and toys which Tim was too ill to use or appreciate, made him cards and picked flowers for his room.

Then suddenly, as happens with children, Tim was better. One minute lying still and silent, utterly drained of energy and life, the next sitting up demanding chicken and chips, lemonade, and *why* can't I go out on my bike *right now*?

Now we were the ones who were drained, eight days and nights of constant attendance, no break and no relief, and suddenly all the household back to normal. We sat back with glazed eyes, and watched it all going on around us. And that, of course, was just the moment for the beloved old guinea pig to turn up her toes.

'She's not moving around much,' says Tina, her carer-in-chief, 'do you think she might have mumps like Tim?' 'I think she's got old age, Tina. Just be gentle with her and try to make sure she's comfortable.'

She watched as tirelessly as we had tended Tim. Sought out the tenderest tips of dandelion, provided extra sweet hay for bedding, touched and stroked as gently as a loving mother with her new-born babe. But nature had to take its course. At last not moving much became not moving at all, and even Tina had to accept her dear pet had gone.

We asked her what she wanted to do now and followed her requests, helped her to say goodbye. Afterwards, she cried a little, then carried on her life as though nothing had happened. No comments, no discussion, no issues arising, not even any change of mood or pace. Well, fine, we thought, after all it was only a guinea pig.

A few days later, though, the situation changed. This was not just a little clouding over, this was huge, billowing, storm-bearing, cumulonimbus monsters blotting out the sky. 'Come and play in the garden, Tina.' 'Don't want to.' 'Then come and play cards.' 'Don't want to.' 'What about just watching telly?' 'Don't want to, all *right*?'

Then, suddenly, she is biting herself. Drawing blood from her hands and arms. Clawing at her face until she looks as though a cat has savaged her. I run to her and pull her to me, sit her on my knee on the settee, cradling her to me and holding her hands. She stiffens, every muscle tense, and starts to scream. It is ear-splitting, this scream, the cry of every abandoned baby in the world gathered together and echoing off the walls of our living room.

I check that I am not gripping her too tightly. In fact my grasp is very light, in reality not holding her at all. Yet it is clearly symbolic, for if I let go she instantly returns to clawing at her face and biting her hands and arms. And the screaming goes on. And on.

If you have never experienced this, and I hope for your sake you have not, you will not be able to grasp fully the horror of it, however true the colours in the picture I paint for you. The scream is deafening, earsplitting, that much must be obvious. But it is an experience involving more than one of the senses. I can feel it in my belly, this scream. My nerve endings vibrate with it.

The tension in her body makes it seem that if I let her go she will leap from my lap and run and run for miles before she drops exhausted. Yet in fact, if I let go my slight hold of her, she stays firmly in place, tearing at her own flesh as though she would flay herself alive.

Minutes pass. Half an hour. Someone brings me a drink. I transfer her two hands to my one, and gratefully drink it, her screaming making my throat feel dry and sore. She makes no response to this. Allows me to hold her safe with just one hand while I refresh myself. But will not herself eat or drink or rest or relax, will not, for more than the moment or two it takes occasionally to draw breath, cease from this awful scream. After an hour, I lift her to her feet, walk with her to the bottom of the garden. She goes with me unprotesting, still intent on her one task of screaming her protest to the universe. Leaning on the fence, looking out over the valley, we give the rest of the household a break from the endless, unremitting sound. The neighbours will have to put up with it, I know the others have to have a chance to hear something else, talk to one another, get themselves to bed in peace.

Brian comes to tell us that supper has been and gone, and the others have all gone to bed. Still utterly passive but for the extreme tenseness of her muscles and the now hoarse but still unending screaming, Tina allows herself to be led back into the house, sits again on my knee, and carries on the process, whatever it is.

Suddenly, from nowhere, there is an ending. Every muscle relaxes, she curls against me, tears pour down her face. 'I want my mum,' she whispers, 'I just want my mum.'

Reproduced from *Attachment, Trauma and Resilience,* by Kate Cairns, published by BAAF in 2002 (pp 20–23). © Kate Cairns

My happy place

Singing Blue Birds
Happy to fly in the sky.
Shiny Gold Fish
From their bowl watch the world go by.
Old Ginger Toms
In sunshine lie.
I a Baby Black Boy
In the wrong family did often cry.
But here is the right place for me to come
And now I am my Daddy's Son.

By Conor Howard, age 8, reproduced from *The Colours in Me,* edited by Perlita Harris and published by BAAF in 2008 (p 76). This anthology presents writing, poetry and artwork by adopted children and young people, giving a vivid insight into their feelings about their adoption experience. © BAAF

Every child is special

I am glad I am adopted, although adoption brings with it feelings of loss, sadness, anger and many, many more feelings it also brings great joy and happiness to everyone involved. My parents were given a chance to have a child they otherwise couldn't have, my biological parents tried to rebuild their lives and I was given a second chance to have a happier life. I would like to say thank you to my family for adopting me and for being the best ever. I love them so much. They have changed my life so much for the better. I could never describe how much.

This extract, by Julia, age 14, is also taken from *The Colours in Me*, as above (p 106). © BAAF

Possible effects of separation and loss

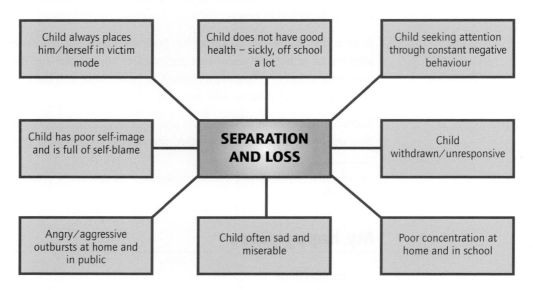

From *Making Good Assessments*, CoramBAAF, 2015

Impact on children of separation and loss

AGE	PRIMARY TASKS	EFFECTS OF LOSS OR MOVE AT THIS STAGE	STRATEGIES FOR HELPING
0–1 year	To develop a sense of trust in the world through needs being met reliably in same way. To organise perceptions of world into meaningful pattern through familiarity and repeated, reliable responses. To develop a strong attachment to one person or small number of familiar people who can act as protection/comfort.	Child's basic sense of trust in the external world is shaken. Child becomes confused/fearful. Child becomes irritable – not easy to comfort through usual methods.	Difficult to prepare child ahead of move because of lack of language. Routines, ways of reacting need to be similar (alter things in new place temporarily) – food. Two "caretakers" need to work together. Need to transfer familiar objects (sounds, smells, touch)
1–3 years	To use a familiar figure as a secure base from which to separate and explore world. To increase self-confidence in order to separate psychologically and physically.	Child loses trust in adult's ability/willingness to protect. Can lead to two reactions a) "clingy" behaviour – child doesn't trust adult not to disappear, therefore, cannot develop appropriate autonomy, ability to separate b) child is remote – parents him/herself – withholds affection – because can't trust adult to parent him or her.	Gradual hand-over of parenting task – help to transfer attachment. Child has some language so can have verbal explanations pre- and post-move. Post-placement contact with previous carers helps reassure child that important people do not just disappear.
3–5 years	To gain increasing independence and self-sufficiency within home – enjoyable separation from caretakers outside home. To question – begin to understand differences between self and others. To move through "magical" thinking to more accurate cause and effect.	Child can blame herself for move 'I wished him dead and made it happen' or for move of others. Child sees self as bad – others as good. Child is not able to achieve levels of self-sufficiency, not able to enjoy independence.	Explain repeatedly – in company with others. Be alert for misconceptions.

AGE	PRIMARY TASKS	EFFECTS OF LOSS OR MOVE AT THIS STAGE	STRATEGIES FOR HELPING
5–10 years	To master problems encountered outside family environment (school, playground, Cubs, etc.) Need to be "freed up" from anxiety about home in order to do this.	Child not able to move on at this stage. May revert to being anxious about leaving home-base. May play with younger children in more secure setting.	Verbal explanations possible. Work on *feelings* – help child identify feelings about move. Involve child in decision-making (appropriately) – gives back some self-confidence and control.
Adoles-cents	To differentiate self from family – move away, develop own values and self controls.	Faced with conflicting tasks a) making new attachments b) moving away May try to do (a) or (b).	Give adolescents as much control as possible whilst providing appropriate protection and support. Use conflict resolution to provide attachment.

MODULE 5:

The needs of children affected by neglect and abuse

Learning outcomes

This module aims to address the following questions:

- What do "neglect" and "abuse" actually mean?
- How does childhood trauma affect attachment and brain development?
- Can children recover?
- What can adoptive parents do to help children recover?
- How does therapy work?

ON NEGLECT

What is neglect?

Think of a child who is dear to you, and make a list of all the things you would want for this child. You are likely to come up with many suggestions which might include 'to feel safe and secure', 'to be loved', 'to have a warm home', 'to be well fed and clothed', 'to be able to play and have fun', 'to go to school', 'to be given opportunities to fulfil their potential', and so on. Isn't this what you want for all children, not just those whom you know and love? If a child lacks one or more of the things you have suggested, does this constitute child neglect? The answer is complicated. Neglect and its impact will depend on the age of the child, the relationship they have with their caregivers, whether it is a one-off omission or commission or something which persists over time alongside other unmet needs. Most parents will admit to a lapse of care or an inadequate response to a child's needs once in a while. But the difference is in the attitude towards and meaning of being a parent and the enduring relationship with the child.

* * *

Cooper (1985) identified a set of basic needs, which remains current today (see below). You may wish to use this framework when thinking of the lives of children you know. Consider what it means to a child if one of these areas of need is unmet.

- **Basic physical care:** *which includes warmth, shelter, adequate food and rest, grooming (hygiene) and protection from danger.*
- **Affection:** *which includes physical contact, holding, stroking, cuddling and kissing, comforting, admiration, delight, tenderness, patience, time, making allowances for annoying behaviour, general companionship and approval.*
- **Security:** *which involves continuity of care, the expectation of continuing in the stable family unit, a predictable environment, consistent patterns of care and daily routine, simple rules and consistent controls and a harmonious family group.*
- **Stimulation and innate potential:** *by praise, by encouraging curiosity and exploratory behaviour, by developing skills through responsiveness to questions and to play, by promoting educational opportunities.*
- **Guidance and control:** *to teach adequate social behaviour which includes discipline within the child's understanding and capacity and which requires patience and a model for the child to copy, for example, in honesty and concern and kindness for others.*

- **Responsibility:** *for small things at first such as self-care, tidying playthings, or taking dishes to the kitchen, and gradually elaborating the decision-making that the child has to learn in order to function adequately, gaining experience through his/her mistakes as well as his/her successes, and receiving praise and encouragement to strive and do better.*
- **Independence:** *to make his/her own decisions, first about small things but increasingly about the various aspects of his/her life within the confines of the family and society's codes. Parents use fine judgement in encouraging independence, and in letting the child see and feel the outcome of his/her capacity. Protection is needed, but over-protection is as bad as too early responsibility and independence.*
(Cooper, 1985, p 31)

Understand what we mean by the term "neglect"

Neglect is not easy to define. Unlike physical or sexual abuse where the definition is centred on an act of abuse, definitions of neglect often focus on omission rather than commission. It is difficult to "see" neglect and the experience of neglect depends on timing (Perry, 2002). For example, infants need touch for survival, teenagers don't. Perry defines neglect as 'the absence of critical organising experiences at key times during development' (p 88). A simple definition might be that a child's needs are not met (Jowitt, 2003). A narrow interpretation of neglect might focus only on physical neglect to the exclusion of emotional neglect. Interpretation may be affected by parental intention and practitioners' understanding of children's needs. Neglect could be a one-off incident, or episodes of neglect or chronic neglect.

It's so difficult, isn't it? It depends on the situation. You can't say that every parent who forgets to send their child to school with the right sports equipment or money or whatever is neglecting them. I know I've done it. But I know sometimes it is neglect.

(Social work assistant)

* * *

Signs that basic needs may be unmet (sources of evidence in italics)

Infants

- Low birth weight; weight faltering *(centile charts, health and midwifery records)*
- Withdrawal from drugs at birth; at risk from blood-borne viruses *(health records)*
- Delay in physical development *(growth charts, health visitor records)*
- Lack of bonding and early attachment *(observation, midwifery and health visitor records)*
- Repetitive, self-soothing movements *(observation, reports from caregivers)*
- Physical signs such as bruises, burns from being left in dirty nappies too long, lesions that have become infected *(observation, health records)*

Pre-school and school age

- Delay in physical growth and development *(health, early years and education records)*
- Delay in cognitive, speech and language development *(health and education records)*

- Behavioural disturbance – excessive aggression, withdrawal, noncompliance, control *(observation, caregiver reports, reports from school)*
- Anxious, insecure attachments to primary caregivers *(observation, attachment checklists, caregiver reports, child reports)*
- Health problems, including hearing and sight difficulties *(school health)*
- Wetting and soiling *(school and health reports)*
- Poor hygiene, smelly and dirty *(observation, reports from school and others, including family members, neighbours)*
- Inappropriate and unsuitable clothing *(observation, reports from school and others)*
- Excessive appetite *(reports from caregivers, school and child; observation)*
- Self-harm *(reports from school, health, caregiver, child; observation)*
- Non-school attendance *(education records)*
- Attending school without proper equipment and clothing *(school reports)*
- Parents/carers do not attend school events *(school records)*
- Poor academic progress *(school reports)*
- Lack of evidence of toys *(observation and questioning)*
- Child not allowed to play outdoors *(child and caregiver reports)*
- Difficulty in forming and keeping relationships with peers *(observation, reports from caregivers, school, child and others)*

Adolescents

Those signs above, plus:

- Anti-social behaviour *(reports from school, community, police)*
- Drug and alcohol use *(observation, reports from caregivers, school, police and others)*
- Being described as "beyond control" *(reports from caregivers, school and others)*
- Going missing, running away *(reports from school, police, caregivers, young person)*

The attachment relationship between the child and their primary caregiver can be the key to identifying neglect. The child with a secure attachment will feel loved, safe and secure, confident of having their needs met and competent to face the world. A sensitive and responsive parent or carer will be attuned to their child's needs and prioritise these. The neglected child is likely to have a difficult attachment relationship with their parent or carer, which often indicates significant unmet needs. If the parent is unable to meet basic needs, the neglected child will feel unsafe, anxious and experience the stress related to unmet need. Observation of the child's behaviour and the way in which child and carer relate to each other can provide valuable information about the attachment relationship. See Fahlberg's attachment checklists (1994, pp 34–37).

One of the common coping mechanisms that neglected children use when they fail to get the required response from their caregivers is to withdraw. These children are often living in environments that are chaotic and disorganised, or depressed and lifeless, with adults who are needy themselves. These are the children who may go unseen and unrecognised; they will try to fade into the background. Rarely do neglected children shout to be heard. They rely on you to recognise them and respond to them.

Reproduced from *Ten Top Tips for Identifying Neglect*, by Pat Beesley, published by BAAF in 2011 (pp 28–37). © BAAF

ON TRAUMA AND RESILIENCE

Traumatic stress

Like all living organisms we generally have an inbuilt preference for survival; for most of their lifespan, living beings seem to endeavour to stay that way. When confronted with a situation which realistically appears to threaten our continued existence, we have an automatic response that greatly enhances our chances of coming out alive. This is known as the traumatic stress response, and the situations which provoke it are known as traumatic events.

Trauma stress has consequences which can lead to mental health problems. It has therefore been a subject of some interest to the medical profession, and there are a number of diagnostic texts which offer definitive statements about trauma, such as the Diagnostic and Statistical Manual of the American Psychiatric Association (1994). Such definitions lead us to conclude that there are two components to traumatic experience.

First there must be an external event, in which the person is confronted with actual or realistically perceived threat to the life or personal integrity of self or others. Then there must be a response to the event which includes fear, helplessness or horror. Thus trauma is by definition a combination of an external event and an internal experience.

Take note that the event may have occurred to "self or others" it is important when looking at the needs of children who have been in situations of domestic violence to recognise that we can be traumatised by witnessing the violation of others. There is some evidence that disorders may be even more common and more severe among those who have witnessed extreme violence, for example, than among the direct victims, however terrible their experience (Harris-Hendrinks *et al*, 2000, p26).

(Cairns, 2002, pp 99–100)

Life with the child

Examples of useful questions

How does this child deal with stress?

Do they turn to others for help when under stress? If so, to whom?

How much stress is too much for them?

Can they express their feelings? When relaxed? When under stress?

Does the child provoke stress in others?

Can they gain comfort from bodily contact with others?

How does the child relax?

What are the basic patterns of sleeping and eating you associate with this child?

Do they get bored easily? Are they comfortable in a low stimulus environment?

Do they try to soothe stress through unusual, compulsive or obsessive behaviours?

Do they try to overcome loss of sensation through stimulating behaviours?

Do they use food, alcohol, drugs or other substances for soothing or stimulation?

How does this child deal with shame?

Do they like to be in control?

Are they comfortable in situations where other people are in charge?

Are they able to accept praise and blame?

Can they take responsibility for their own actions?

Are they able to rejoin the group after they have caused offence to others?

WHAT CAN WE DO?: approaches to living and working with children with unmet attachment needs

The four step plan

Step 1: commitment

Each child needs us to commit ourselves to sharing a journey with them, a journey which we undertake in the full knowledge that it will change us forever. It is impossible to provide an authentic and trustworthy relationship without accepting that measure of vulnerability. Unlike the child, you will have undertaken the journey freely and of your own volition. It is important to remember this if the going gets tough and the enterprise seems overwhelming. Sharing for a while the life journey of children with unmet attachment needs can be a great adventure, it can stretch us to levels of creativity and endurance we had not known we could produce, but it can also be destructive. For in human social relationships, the very forces which are creative are also those which destroy.

We will be required to establish empathy with the child. Some of the time, and it must be only some of the time, we will need to experience the world as the child does. This will produce a dizzying sense of dislocation, followed, if all goes well, by an expansion of perspective. We will come to understand that the world may, at a fundamental level, be different from our most basic assumptions about it. This is what Gregory Bateson called "level three learning" (2000); it is learning which disrupts not merely how we think about the world, but the basic mental constructs that let us learn to think about the world. Level three learning changes us radically. It picks apart and remakes the patterns which shape and contain our understanding.

If you are unable to offer this commitment, do not undertake the work. It will damage you. If the adventure is for you, then proceed to step two.

Step 2: personal support

It is essential when living and working with children with unmet attachment needs that we establish and maintain our own close, confiding, intimate relationships. This is the source of our own sanity and is a resource to sustain our own resilience. The work will challenge and may destroy both. It will also challenge the durability and flexibility of our own secure attachments. It is vital that we pay attention to these relationships, giving at least as much attention to relationships which are mutual and reciprocal and sustaining as to those which are more problematic, more demanding and which will be a net drain on our resources.

It is not enough to think about these personal relationships before you set off on the journey with the child and then forget about them. We live in a dynamic universe, and everything changes. You need to keep paying attention to these relationships, and to other close, confiding, mutual relationships which may form, and to treat these as having a higher priority even than your work with the child.

These relationships are not only a source of support for you, they are the check and balance, monitoring that you are not changing in harmful ways. Dan Hughes (1997, p 214) says that if we join the child everybody loses, but if the child joins us everybody wins. As we keep the child company on their journey, change happens. You will not be the same person at the end as you were at the beginning, and neither will the child. It is imperative that all the change is in the direction of building attachment and not in the direction of destroying it. Yet the powerful experience of this work can result in us losing our way and going with the child into their own cold and frightening world. What we want is to enable a terrified child to enter safely into the warmth of secure attachments.

As well as the changes which occur in your life as a result of your work with the child, close relationships also change in their own right, they have a dynamic life of their own. Again it is important to keep an eye on all the relationships in your social network, to ensure that you are not overtaken by events, finding yourself alone and friendless just when you most need a supporting presence.

If you do not with reasonable certainty have the protection of close, confiding, intimate relationships to sustain and support you reliably throughout the time you are giving commitment to the child, then do not proceed with the work. It will damage you. If you do have access to trustworthy and intimate others who are reliable sources of mutual support and joy, then go on to step three.

Step 3: professional supervision

Whatever your role in providing for the needs of children with unmet attachment needs, you must ensure that you have access to professional supervision. It is even more important that direct carers – parents, family network caregivers, adopters and foster carers – have access to professional supervision and support than it is for child care professionals whose work with the children is not carried out in their own life space.

Those who are closest to us will provide the core support which will keep us sane and resilient. But they will not be able reliably to provide the essential overview of the system which will reveal the direction in which we are moving, will alert us to any risks, and will propose systemic solutions which will be beyond the scope of our own vision; we cannot see the ocean when we are swimming in it. Only the professional supervisor can take on this function.

You may be fortunate enough to have clear structures of accountability which provide appropriate supervision in your work with the child. If not, it is necessary to find a supervisor for yourself and to submit yourself to a discipline which may often be uncomfortable but which will be essential for your safety and the safety of your family. Since this relationship too will be dynamic, it is important to keep the situation under scrutiny, and to make sure that your needs are met throughout the whole time of your commitment to the child.

Over the course of the changing relationship with the child, even people who have access to professional structures of supervision may from time to time benefit from external consultation. Although professional and external to your immediate relationships, supervision or consultation may be provided in many ways. It may not necessarily be frequent, it need not be costly if you are relying on your own funds, and it should be set within clear boundaries. It may be provided by any agency employing people with the skill and knowledge to assess the health of family systems and the progress of reparative work in the field of attachment. When you have reasonable certainty of being provided with sources of professional supervision, it will be possible to move on to step four.

Step 4: working with others to build an environment which promotes secure attachment

All those who have made a commitment to the child now have to work together to construct an environment which will enable the child to move from the cold and lonely wasteland of unmet attachment needs to the warmth and safety and supportiveness of secure attachment relationships.

This environment must meet both the need for affective attunement and the need for reintegrative shame. It will be an environment in which all those close to the child are adopting a consistent approach which meets the child's needs, adapting the approach to fit their own role with the child, but providing great consistency in the basic structures surrounding the child. It will be an environment which respects the child as a unique and infinitely valuable individual with certain inalienable rights, and which also assumes that the child is a social being, born sociable and lovable, and able to discover their own sociability and their own lovable nature if liberated from overwhelming anxiety and shame.

Secure attachment arises out of parenting, where parenting is seen as the activities of the community into which the child is born that ensure that the needs of the child are met. When this social structure is in some way disrupted or challenged, there may need to be help for the immediate caregivers from the wider community, which we might consider to be preventive parenting. Such preventive parenting will enable the child to develop secure attachments despite the challenges; this may apply when babies are born with some impairment, or when parents or other caregivers experience illness or accident or trauma.

When children have suffered injury as a result of the developmental disruption, however, and have formed insecure attachments, then there will need to be more structured help from the community. This could be described as therapeutic parenting. It is parenting which aims to enable the child to move from insecure to secure attachment. If all else fails, it may be necessary for the child to be placed with new carers, and possibly also in an entirely new social environment. This I shall call therapeutic reparenting.

Parenting which has a therapeutic purpose, where there is an intentional effort to promote change in attachment patterns, is, like all parenting, a social phenomenon. It consists of the activities through which the community provides for the needs of the child to be met, but those needs now include the need for reparative work in relation to attachment. It is what is provided when those who have committed themselves to the child work together to construct a therapeutic environment for the child.

Therapeutic parenting and reparenting both require the creation of a formal care team around the child. The informal social structures which will sustain child development and prevent injury for securely attached children are not adequate to meet the needs of children with unmet attachment needs. Parenting insecurely attached children is often counterintuitive; carers have to *learn* how to approach children who beyond infancy are unable to regulate stress and impulse, and they have to be reliably sustained in maintaining that approach. That is the task of the care team.

The child will need insightful interventions at every level of the social system. Health care, education, community activities, the justice system, counsellors and therapists, and every other service provider right through to central government, where the legal structures are created within which these services are provided, will all be contributing to the outcome of the reparenting. This is the ecology of human development described by Bronfenbrenner (1979).

Reproduced from *Attachment, Trauma and Resilience*, by Kate Cairns, published by BAAF in 2002 (pp 57–71). © Kate Cairns and BAAF

Fear

Rachel, aged three: *'Time for bed.' 'But the fox might eat me.' 'Which fox?' 'The one in my room.' We search the room together, trusting small hand gripping mine. Under the bed, in the cupboard, behind the curtains. 'I think he's not here. You can go to bed now.' Three-year-old's bedtime rituals complete, I give a goodnight kiss. 'Sleep well. Sweet dreams.' ''Night, mum. Leave the light on.'*

Jay: *'When I was five, my dad used to belt me every day. And I was, like, really violent at school. So they sent me away to a boarding school. I was six then. At that place, if I shouted out in the night, I was dragged out of bed and put in a little room called the snug. Just a stone floor and nothing to do. Once there was snow outside, and I was left there from half past five in the morning until breakfast time.'*

Begin, as I must, with the scream in the dark. One terrified cry: 'no...o...o!' Threads of fear from the nightmare reach out through the house, chilling me in my warm bed. I grope for the clock; just after three, not the worst night we've had. Wait now, five minutes, ten minutes; then the coughing starts. Five minutes more and a tap at the door.

I go out to the landing. He is 15 years old, taller than me by a full head, all bones and adolescent angles, shy placatory smile warding off peril.

'Sorry to wake you. I can't sleep. This cough is terrible. Can you give me something for it?' The smile is belied by the eyes – dear God, who left you with terrors like this? – it hurts me to look at his eyes. I put an arm around him, 'It's all right, I don't sleep much, you go back to bed and I'll bring you a warm drink.'

When I arrive with the drink, he is huddled under the covers in a foetal position, shivering. The room smells of fresh cigarette smoke, the window wide open and letting in a gale.

Closing the window, 'I thought perhaps you'd had a bad dream?' 'No. I never dream. It's just this cough that woke me.' 'Do you think you'll sleep now?' 'Mm.' 'Well, I'll be awake for a while. Come and find me if you need me.'

Back in my warm, safe bed, Brian snuggles up to me. 'One of Jay's nightmares?' 'Yes.' 'Will you wait till he's settled?' 'Yes, I'll read for a while.' As dawn breaks, I know we've had an easier night than some, and drift off to sleep.

By seven, the others are tucking into breakfast, relishing the one time of day they know they can share untroubled. 'Bad night?' – this from Rachel, over her shoulder, bleached blonde hair skimming her cereal as she does a quick check, registers baggy eyes and dragging feet. 'Aren't they all?'

'Let him sleep,' she says, 'give us some peace. I'll drop him at school on my way to work.' 'Can I have a lift too?' this from Tim, a few months younger than Jay, vulnerable I know, but what can I do? 'If you don't want your bike at school.' I watch him thinking, weighing the issues, even a simple lift becomes complicated.

'No, I'll ride.' And he reaches over, punches David on the arm, 'Check my maths for me?' Gentle David looks up from his otherworld, slaps his little brother – tall as he is and twice as wide – on the back of the head. 'Bring it to my room. We'll have a look at it.' They amble amiably away. Rachel hugs me. 'You take Jay a drink, and I'll get one for Dad.'

I knock on the door and go in. In sleep I can see his face clearly, his features relaxed, his expression peaceful. Waking, tension distorts and bunches the lines of his face, his eyes never free from terror or rage. I lean over and touch him gently on the shoulder, waking him softly, 'Jay, a drink for you.' Anything sharper and he will spring into life as a soldier under fire will wake to a sound. He opens his eyes and smiles, 'Mum! Thanks.' I'm not his mum, but in the half-sleep it's close enough, and all the comfort he'll have.

Now there's no rest till he's ready for school. He is as needy as a baby, as dependent as an infant, as touchy as a toddler. 'Where's my...?' 'Who's got...?' 'Somebody's taken my...!' The others go to earth, waiting for the morning storm to pass. At last Rachel shoos him out the door, and David and Tim emerge, still arguing differential equations, to make their own less frazzled way to school.

A quick coffee with Brian, and I'm at the telephone for my morning call, so routine by now I could put it on a tape recorder, responses and all. We need help with this child. Promises were made to us, all of them broken, that we should have full support, everything we needed to make the placement work.

There was a time in our work when such promises meant something, when we safely took into our home and our hearts children whose battered lives and wounded spirits could find comfort and healing in a peaceful environment. But those days have gone, now the same needs stretch us to the limit and beyond, as those who once supported us have had their own work redefined. Once we could share the burden, which then became no burden; now priorities have changed, services reduced, and we are left dangerously exposed as the objects of attachment for seriously wounded children.

'She's in a meeting at the moment. I'll ask her to ring you.' 'Tell her it's urgent.' (Tell her I'm falling apart. Tell her we're desperate. TELL HER TO READ MY LETTERS!) 'She'll ring you within an hour.' I say thank you nicely, the way I was taught, but know I won't be holding my breath for the 'phone call. Promises butter no parsnips, speaking of which, there are things to be doing.

A few tasks on, and the telephone rings. A miracle? No, the school head of year. Jay has attacked a boy during the games lesson, and needs to be picked up. Ever since his last suicide attempt, when the psychiatrist said he was too traumatised for psychotherapy to be anything but dangerous, Jay has been accepted at school on the basis of a special arrangement whereby if things get too tough he can come home at any time.

At school, Jay is with the nurse. This attack, unlike others, was actually minor. Friends saw Jay start to "flip" and held him back from doing any great damage. But he is sitting huddled in the chair, shaking uncontrollably and hot to the touch. 'I'm sorry! I'm sorry! I didn't mean to!' Then he looks up, searches my face, 'I wanted to kill him. I really wanted to kill him. What's wrong with me?' I can't answer that, certainly not now, not here. The school staff have been wonderful; he is so able, so eager to learn and do well, they have made space for him, and, so far, he has not been excluded. Let's not push our luck. I soothe him, thank them, and take him home.

Five minutes in the car, and the verbal torrent starts. My driving, my looks, my age, my relationship with Brian, my tastes, my friends, all are targets for the stream of jibes. I stonewall, focus my attention on the person behind the words, stay peaceable. As we get into the house, I stop him, turn him to face me, 'You're pushing me, Jay. Why are you doing that?' 'It's fun. Winding the staff up – it's what I'm good at.' 'So what happens then?' 'They send you away. Send you to your room. Tell you to get out of the Unit.' 'Do you want me to send you away?' 'NO!' I look at him and smile. He grins, laughs, grabs me in a bear hug. 'You're too little to hug properly.' 'Perhaps you're too big. You should have been with us sooner. Lots of child-hugs on offer here.' He moves away from me, looks at me full in the face, 'I got lost on the way.' Ain't *that* the truth.

Peaceful now, we make cakes for tea. Yet still he is anxious, scanning my face and body language constantly for signs of displeasure, checking his progress with the simple tasks, belittling his own abilities. Then the mood changes, tension begins to build. I glance at the clock; the others will soon be home, more people to relate to, more mistakes to make.

I leave him clearing up and go to water the hanging baskets, knowing he will follow. As he comes round the side of the house, I spray him with water. Our game. He runs, and I chase him. He laughs, shouts, grabs me and wrestles the spray from me. Now he chases, I run. He catches me and sprays me. 'Right,' I say, 'we're quits now.' His face sets, he whisks the top from the spray and empties a stream of water over my head, drenching me. Then he steps back, trembling, begging me with his eyes not to be angry. 'Did I win?' 'Yes, Jay, you won.' 'Is that all right? You're not angry?' 'It's fine, Jay. It's a game. Now why don't you go and see if you can win against the computer?' He runs off happily, and I go and change my clothes.

Back in the kitchen, Tim arrives home and I ask, 'Good day?' 'So so. Where's Jay?' Always the first question. 'Playing on the computer.' He can relax now, slumped down, long legs stretched out, munching fresh cakes and chatting about school, the casting for the school play, what to take as an audition piece. David arrives, both boys love to be on stage, wander off together to rehearse.

Rachel and Brian arrive together as the meal is ready. Both look the question they will not ask in case the news is bad. I tell them about the attack in school, no injuries this time, Jay calmed down by an afternoon at home. Rachel goes to fetch the boys, David lost in a book, Tim and Jay now playing together on the computer.

For once the meal goes calmly, no tantrums, no upsets. We enjoy each other's company. During washing up, though, Jay begins to niggle at Tim, punching, pinching, flicking with the tea towel. Tim takes it for a while, then goes off to watch television. I listen, but it sounds as though things have settled; leaving the household to its own devices, I curl up in an armchair with coffee and a crossword puzzle.

Brian, angrily, 'That boy is nothing but a walking bloody penis!' We stare at one another, appalled. The way we learn what we already knew. 'I just meant he's so arrogant, so cocky, you know?' I do know, exactly. What, specifically, provoked this, though? Half an hour of non-stop baiting of Tim, who at last has gone to his room, too angry to talk to anyone. 'Do something, Kate, talk to Jay. Get him to back off.' Brian shakes his head, bewildered, used to taking an equal part but here frustrated and held at a distance by Jay's evident and intractable fear of all men.

I sigh, and go to look for Jay. Finding him in the living room, staring into space, I say I need to talk to him. He glares at me. I start in on how he's been pushing at Tim again, making his life unbearable, about how we need to respect one another, and give one another breathing space. Suddenly he shouts, 'I don't understand! What do you want? I don't know what you want from me! Do you want a fucking blow job or what?'

I'm speechless. Then he looks at me, sees me at last. 'You've gone red. What is it? What's the matter?' 'I'm embarrassed and angry,' I say, as calmly as I can. 'I'm embarrassed because you've crossed that line we've talked about before. You can talk to me about anything, including sex, but you may not talk to me as though I was your age, or anything other than I am. I am an adult who is responsible for you and who cares for you, and I take that responsibility seriously. I will not abuse you and nor will anyone here. Do you understand me?' Face hidden in a cushion, voice thick with tears. 'Yes.'

'I'm angry because I've been trying to talk to you about not hurting other people, and you are not listening to me. You have been pushing Tim beyond the limit, and you have to stop. Are you listening to me now?'

'Yes. I know it's wrong. I'm sorry.' Then suddenly, bursting out, 'It's just, Tim's like me, you know, I feel close to him, I feel I have the right.' 'So you feel close to Tim, he reminds you of yourself, so you feel it is all right to treat him as you've been treated?' 'A bit. Yes.'

Now the cushion comes down from the face. He acknowledges that he does not have the right to make Tim a victim, and does not truly want to do so. We discuss strategies for his coping. Using the punchbag. Going for a bike ride. Going to his room. I know he means it, know too that the problem for him is in recognising his own actions, coming to terms with his own moods and the feelings which drive him.

'Can I go to Youth Club?' 'Of course.' 'I don't think I... My foot hurts, can I have a lift?' I smile at him. 'It wasn't too painful for football earlier. What's the real problem?' 'You know.' 'Say it, Jay. It's nothing to be ashamed of.' 'I get scared. You know. Walking on my own.' 'Then I'll give you a lift. Go and get ready.'

At half-past-nine I pick him up from the Club. Park at the other side of the car park to see him walk across. Pretty steady on his feet. Test the air as he gets into the car; marijuana, I think, no sign of anything stronger tonight. A few days ago it was petrol ('Hey, I've discovered the meaning of life. It's something to do with...', puzzled, '...roundabouts?') Before that it was speed, acid, sometimes ecstasy, sometimes alcohol. Brian says, 'Where does he get the money?' – another remark that leaves us staring at each other, speechless.

At home, he gets ready for bed, comes down in his dressing gown, limping. 'My foot really does hurt.' 'What's wrong with it?' 'I think it's... what do you call it...an ingrowing toenail. Will you look at it for me?' I go with him to the bathroom. The toe has been hacked and chopped about, is oozing blood and pus. 'What happened here?' 'I was trying to stop it from hurting.' I wash it gently and put on a dressing, then send him off to bed. 'Come up and say goodnight?' 'Of course, if you like.'

Downstairs, Brian has opened a bottle of wine for us to share with Rachel. David and Tim wander down to watch the news with us and share a quiet half hour. This night unusually peaceful. No police on the doorstep. No sitting up waiting for the worst effects of substance abuse to pass. No storms and tantrums, leaving windows and doors to repair. Just a little time to relax and draw breath before we see what nightmares the new night may bring.

But first, a promise to keep. I tap on the door. He is sitting in bed, sticking football stickers in a scrapbook. His music is on, but not too loud. It really is an unusually peaceful night. I kiss him on the forehead.

'Good night, sweetheart. Remember we all love you.'

'I know. Thanks. I love you too. Leave the light on.'

Reproduced from *Attachment, Trauma and Resilience*, by Kate Cairns, published by BAAF in 2002 (pp 14–20). © Kate Cairns

ON THERAPEUTIC INTERVENTION AS PART OF POST-ADOPTION SUPPORT

Therapies

Sometimes a child's emotional and behavioural difficulties are such that some adopters and their children need and benefit from therapeutic help from a professional outside the family.

Many different therapies are used in post-adoption support. They all aim to get you to the same place, but will take you there by different routes. Effective interventions in post-adoption support are those that include the parents as equal partners.

Sometimes – if the situation is very intense – it might be helpful for the child to have individual therapy (from someone with experience in attachment and developmental issues and post-abuse work) and for the parents to have consultation.

Parents sometimes source a therapist for themselves and this may become more common in the future when direct payments or personal payments are available. Some CAMHS (Child and Adolescent Mental Health Services) can provide therapists but availability is variable and CAMHS has increasingly moved to a consultation model.

Therapies can include family therapy, behaviour therapy, play therapy, counselling, psychoanalysis and art/music/drama therapies, and can be beneficial for both adult and child.

Much of the therapeutic work needed for adopted children lies in the realm of post-abuse work and repair through attuned, sensitive, robust and supported parenting. A therapist undertaking this work should have that awareness and be prepared to work alongside parents as well as with the child.

Some children have experienced things that no child should ever have to live through. Just hearing about the neglect and abuse that some children are subjected to may be upsetting and disturbing for you. Children don't come through these experiences unscathed. But with the help of adults (both adopters and professionals) who understand the impact of trauma and have learned how to help, they can recover and adapt to their difficulties. If you go on to adopt a child, you can learn more about this. You could be the one to turn a child's life around.

Unlocking trauma through music and art

It has taken time for our boys to attach to each other. I am not suggesting that they have a healthy strong relationship, but they are certainly not indifferent to each other. Starting from a month-long honeymoon, which quickly sank into mutual loathing, they somehow grew to respect each other; loyalty developed and a bond, albeit shaky, was created. Now we are in the trivial bickering and the occasional thumping each other phase. But the other night Joe read two chapters of *The Hobbit* to Jack. A lot can happen – it doesn't just happen overnight; it is a process, full of ups and downs and merry go-rounds.

The key to unlocking the boys' trauma was Joy's music and art. Without her we would never have had the confidence to challenge Joe's and Jack's perceptions of the world. In their own ways they both created a bubble around themselves, which is what we all do if we are threatened. But their bubbles excluded intimacy and close relationships. Joy's music, and to some extent art, helped us to penetrate their bubbles. We went to her as a family out of rhythm and out of tune, each making our own sound but not keeping time or making music together. If we played instruments together today it wouldn't be perfect, but it would be more co-operative, more fun, more open and trusting. We would enjoy it.

As much as I would love to say that therapists like Joy perform miracles and cure your child, I can't. She hasn't "cured" either of our boys, but she did make a difference. Looking back, I'm not sure we would have survived as a family without her, and I am quite sure about the positive impact therapy had on both boys, but especially on Joe, because he needed something powerful and fundamental to shift his perception of the world adults create. There has been a gradual, and I mean gradual because it is still very much "work in progress", improvement in how Joe communicates. He looks people in the eye and he tries to connect instead of retreating into his detached, cut off world. He no longer wants to be hollow. He wants some of the good feelings we all get when we click with fellow human beings.

Joe is lucky because he is good looking and has a rather quirky sense of humour and is reasonably bright. As he makes his way through the turmoil of the teenage years, we are watching him turn into a person who wants to live a full life. He recently said to me, 'I don't want to be on the edge any more'. Joy helped him join the human race.

There are still issues for Joe. He still has difficulty asking for help, often puts up barriers to protect himself against possible rejection, can appear to have an attitude, lacks empathy and can be entirely wrapped up in himself. Some of this is normal adolescence and some has roots further back. We can help him grow, but in the end we can't change his past and the emotional disability it has left him. He is recovering but it is a life-long task. With Joy's help, we have merely equipped him better for his journey.

Jack is very different indeed. He worked with Kate, the art therapist, as much as he worked with Joy. Kate skilfully helped Jack to see himself as a whole person, rather than Jack the clown, whose only role in life was messing around, making others laugh and hiding behind his cute smile.

They worked together on building up a beautiful picture of his life story, which helped him get the facts straight but never touched, moved or engaged him emotionally. We will soon be taking a trip back to see Joy.

Jack's schoolwork has improved slightly during his three years with us. He can concentrate better and does read a bit, but should be achieving more. No one had been able to pinpoint why he wasn't learning until a few weeks ago, when he told me how his birth father physically threatened him when he was unable to remember his letters and numbers. He is afraid that a mistake will put his life in danger. Every time he tries to read he has to cope with all the feelings his birth father aroused in him. So we are going back to see Joy in the hope that she can release him from his terror and, who knows, that may help his learning difficulties.

For me, every aspect of therapy has been worth it because of all the support and practical advice we have had. Joy was able to explain behaviour that seemed outrageous and beyond our understanding. Initially we participated in the boys' therapy sessions, but more lately Ed and I have attended workshops organised by Joy and her team. These have proved invaluable because so much has been discovered about trauma and how it affects a child's development generally, and more specifically, the infant brain; how the effects of emotional neglect and abuse disable a child from using this most vital part of their body. It relegates parts of their brain to a wheelchair, disables them intellectually as with Jack, or emotionally, as with Joe.

Reproduced from *Together in Time*, by Ruth and Ed Royce, published by BAAF in 2008 (pp 142–144).
© Ed Royce

Bottom of a bottle

From whenever it is that my very first memory is, it's of me being a very smiley, content and all-round happy kid. Mum and me went places and did things together; always together. I was very happy. I had everything I wanted and it all seemed great. The few minor upsets, like sitting on a wasp and getting stung, were miniscule specks of black upon a clear white background of my early years, on this seemingly innocent, good natured and nice little life of mine.

Yeah. I had everything – all the toys, my family that looked after me and places I could go. My first bike that I rode into a park gate and well near brained myself on. My big brother's lead soldiers that they would never let me touch in case I started sucking on one and received lead poisoning from the well-crafted metal monsters that always looked so good, and captivated my imagination and attention every time I was in my sister's father's house. I would sit in our two-bedroom flat and play with the batman and the various other toys I had for ages, most of the day. Just let me go and off I went. And I would go for the whole day. I was fine like that.

Mum would seem to bring random guys home sometimes. At the time I didn't fully understand this, only the feeling that they would stay for a while. Well, of course, now I know that she was after another guy to replace my father after he ran away. She went in and out of relationships with several people. People that I never quite felt were particularly good people. Didn't know why at the time, but now I guess that somewhere in my childish mind I could sense that they were just like my mother. Addicted to alcohol and getting drunk on it. Like her they stared into empty cans and bottles, trying to get the very last drops into their alcohol infested blood.

The only difference was that my mother had tried her best to stop, stop for me. But in the end I guess she found it just that bit too hard to stop drinking herself into stupors. The alcohol was too deeply ingrained in her and eventually she went down, taking me with her.

It's strange how I can still remember the three promises she gave me when I was growing up. Still a toddler about three years old, but I still remember:

'I promise you I will always look after you,

I will always care and I will never hit you.'

She broke all three. With the days and nights of continuous drinking and sleeping, the small lapses in between, where she would stagger around drunkenly looking for another can, she broke every promise she made to me. I can still remember vividly the time I spent alone in that flat whilst she slept for another day or two. I can remember it all too well.

It was sunny, I was in the front room playing with the batmobile I had received last Christmas only a few months previous. She came in and told me we were going up the road. I put on my shoes and coat and off we went to the top of the hill, where a row of shops stood overlooking the road. I thought we would go into the post office. It was the only shop we had ever been in, out of all the shops on that small strip of pavement. Instead I was dragged past it. Immediately I was very confused. Where was Mum going?

We turned into a small shop. There were row upon row of shelves. All filled to the brim with all sorts of cans – gold, blue, black. I grew all the more puzzled as to why we were in here instead of the post office. She walked quickly over to six cans held together with some sort of thin semi-clear plastic. Lifted them up and took them to the counter.

Suddenly I was on edge. A small flare of imminent danger and warning blared in my infantile mind. I didn't like this shop with its dingy, crowded looking cans and shelves. I wanted out. We went out, back into the sunlight of the early spring morning. Suddenly the sunlight didn't look so pleasing and neither did the clear blue sky, which held it. All I could think was that those cans were bad news.

We walked back to the tall, dirty block of flats. It's crazy, but until then I had never noticed how run down and bad the place looked. It was only through the buying of those cans that I started to notice the small pockets of darkness. And suddenly my nice clean background had many more dots of black on it.

We got back in and I watched Mum set the cans down on the floor. All except one. Once more the warning went off in the back of my head. I didn't want to see those cans any more, so I went into the front room to play. In fact I was scared of those golden cans. Not like the fear after a nightmare or the fear that a monster was going to lurch into my room and devour me, after watching one too many horror themed cartoons. This was like a wake-up call. It signalled that real fear like nothing I had ever experienced was about to open its eyes and grip me with its terrifying gaze. This fear was terrible and deep. It went right through me and sucked out the happiness. Even my toys could not distract me. I couldn't drive away the thought of my mother standing there with a long gold can clutched in her hand.

I went out into the hallway to go to my room. The cans were not there. More fear swept through me. I decided to seek out the cans. I looked into my mum's room. There she was lying on her bed sprawled like a shot bird. Around her crumpled form were six cans, open and laying side on. This time no panic or fear swept through me. She was sleeping. It was fine. There was nothing wrong; she must have simply been thirsty. With the thoughts of normality softly blocking out the fear that had constricted on me only moments before, I returned to the front room and the TV, totally unaware that there was no more normality. No more everyday. Totally unknowing that my small world was about to go from peaceful and filled to empty and chaotic.

These words seem like a complete contradiction and seemingly make no sense at all, but that's what it was like. Over the weeks I spent alone, with myself and a woman who only got up to buy some more beer and drink herself back into a coma that would last from one to three days, I did realise that something was wrong with her. I also realised there was nothing I could do. So I did what I could for myself. I got drinks by climbing onto the kitchen table and pouring the contents of a bottle into a dirty glass, which I used repeatedly. I could get nothing to eat as food was in the fridge and the handle was out of reach. So I would wait for my mother to resurface, still drunk, stagger from her room and bring me a plate of cheese and crackers every few days, if she remembered.

By now she had broken two of her promises. 'Looking after me' and 'caring' had been washed from her lips by the alcohol running out of her mouth, as she drank herself past consciousness. At about the one-month mark she broke the third, 'I will never hit you.' I was on my way to the kitchen; it was about noon and I was in the hall. She appeared in front of me and I looked up at her with a happy smile, pleased that she had raised herself after the three-day sleep. She looked down at me with an unknowing, blank, intoxicated stare. She grabbed me and started hitting me.

I had no idea why and nor did I care. She had just broken her last promise. The hitting faded into the background as the emotional realisation hit me. It hit me harder than anything I have ever felt. I was crushed completely. That was the last shard of hope I had clung to, the last thread that might have symbolised an end to what was happening. She snapped it. She tore it in two like a dirty rag and threw it away. I broke away and ran to my room and sat there motionless against the door. I felt empty, angry, confused and broken. She had shattered my hope. There was no coming back from this. She didn't care. She didn't want to. She was wrapped up in the alcohol and there was no space for anything else.

For the next month I did what I had done before: carried on as usual. But there was a difference. This time everything lacked its previous enjoyment and spirit; there was no drive in it and no happiness, just a gaping empty pit where my happiness used to be. I played quietly without expression, my face blank with staring empty eyes. When I watched TV I didn't laugh or find it entertaining. I watched it because I could do nothing else. My plain white background was now completely black. I'm unclear how long I went on like this. It's blurry and confused.

I was sitting watching TV, the same emptiness and the same pain. The same confusion, the same fear and the same anger all surrounding me and enveloping me like a blanket, crushing out everything good. Still I sat there unmoving, not laughing, uncaring. Nothing seemed to matter any more. My mum didn't care, there was nothing to eat and all that was left was a cold empty shell of the child I once was.

I was sitting there like that when there was a loud thump on the door. Danger. My first instinct was danger. I chose the first suitably sheltering thing I could see to hide in: the table. So I crouched under the table, scared and wondering what was happening. And my mother appeared, staggering over to the door and opening it. I went and stood behind her. People. Two people. They towered above me and started talking to what was my mother. One of them asked me to take one thing with me, so I went into my room and on the end of my bed was the stuffed toy I had had since I was first born. I picked it up and made to leave. She stopped me.

'Don't you want this one too?' she asked, waving another that I had grown quite attached to, but seemed a lot less meaningful. I nodded and my mother looked at them with pleading eyes. They nodded and I was taken out onto the balcony into the night, down the foul looking stairs and put into a car. I sat in the back and as the car started I took one look back at the towering flats looming in the dark night sky. The car started moving and I turned away with only the thought that I knew I would never see the place I had called home again. Neither would I see the person I called mum and the thing I called life...

This event changed me catastrophically. A large part of my happiness and stability was torn out because of this; I'm left with scars and a lot of personal pain and anger. However, for all the pain, the anger, insecurity and everything else it left me, I feel stronger for it. This gave me a determination and strength to take everything else that was thrown at me after that, and even things that will be coming my way in future. I guess it could be described with the phrase 'Whatever doesn't kill you makes you stronger'.

I'm also a lot more aware of how badly drink can mess up your life and the lives of people around you. Things like this always have shockwaves that will destroy whatever isn't directly affected by someone's mess. Although I was the most affected, I wasn't the only one to be damaged by her addiction.

I don't think I will ever get over that. I will always have that with me, as much as I could try to put it in the back of my mind and forget about it, it's always going to be there and it's always going to hurt. So I can try and live with it, despite everything it has given me.

This extract, by Francis Davies, written at age 16, is reproduced from *The Colours in Me*, edited by Perlita Harris and published by BAAF in 2008 (pp 14–18). © BAAF

How I can help promote the child's resilience

....

....

....

....

....

....

....

....

....

....

....

....

....

....

....

....

....

....

....

....

....

MODULE 6: **Becoming a parent through adoption**

Learning outcomes

This module aims to help you to:

- **think about why you want to adopt**
- **think more broadly about the child or children you might go on to adopt**
- **consider how you might meet the needs of a child when he or she is first placed with you**
- **consider the impact adoption will have on your lifestyle and your family life**

ON EXPECTATIONS AND THE REALITY

Life after placement

- What picture do you have of life as a parent?
- What do you expect of your adopted child?
- Adjusting to the reality

Every prospective adoptive parent...will hold their own particular fantasies of how they will fulfil their new role. They will have not only their visions of success but also the anticipation of how soon they will achieve this – often much more easily and quickly than will be experienced in reality. Knowledge of the extent of children's past hurts may fuel their expectations of "making these better". Thus, awareness of likely difficult behaviour may be mirrored by their anticipation of understanding fully a child's feelings, concerns and needs and being able to reason with them about appropriate ways of expressing these. The more strongly and deeply such parenting fantasies exist, the more difficult it will be for new parents/carers to deal with the many disappointments they will then face. To the reality of the child's complex emotional responses may be added the bitterness of the new parent's ruined expectations.

For all applicants, a continuing personal re-evaluation of what to expect of themselves as well as the child will be essential, informed by a more realistic adjustment of their preconceptions of parenting with the likely realities of life after placement. Applicants will need to remember there is no such thing as a perfect parent, only a "good enough" one who can admit to their faults, learn from their mistakes, enjoy their successes, and who constantly tries to improve and grow as a parent.

From *Making Good Assessments* by Pat Beesley, published by CoramBAAF, 2015. © CoramBAAF

ON THE IMPACT ON YOUR LIFESTYLE AND YOUR FAMILY LIFE

Extended families

Your parents will become grandparents to your adopted child; your brothers and sisters will become uncles and aunts. How can they help?

Extended family members may be very enthusiastic about meeting an adopted child but, for the sake of not overwhelming the child with new people, they may need to be patient and wait until the child has settled in and got to know his or her new parents first. Later on, practical help, such as help with housework or preparing meals, may be very much appreciated, especially if the adopters have a sibling group.

You will need to consider whether your extended family members are ready to welcome the child into the family or whether they may have reservations (either privately or openly), especially if the child is seen to be "difficult". Transracial adoptions too may raise complex issues in some extended families.

You could be their big sister!

The idea of adoption had filtered in and out of my life since I was a child; for James, however, not so: adoption was never going to happen; he couldn't ever see himself having someone else's child; how could he ever feel the same as he did about his perfect little girl? I wanted him to drive us forward, for someone else to be at the steering wheel. But at this point in time James was prepared, content even, for Daisy to be his only child. So would he stop us in our tracks? Would I let him? Did I love him enough to do so without resentment? Surely a daddy, Daisy's daddy, and my husband were more important than anything else? How could I even be thinking these things when we had her to consider?

Those dark moments still pass through my memory every so often. How could two people so much in love, and with Daisy to show for it, feel so far away from one another when all they ever wanted was to create a family? Quite obviously we were not ready to adopt. Besides, whilst there was no concrete explanation for our infertility there was still a chance, right? And it was that "chance" that continued to loom over Daisy for a good while yet.

Daisy was at nursery school, only months from starting school, and perhaps not quite so much my baby any more. Einstein, our lanky chocolate labrador retriever, who incidentally is great at snoring on sofas but utterly useless at retrieving, had very contentedly taken his rather hairy, distinctly smelly place in the family, offering a wonderfully gentle, if a little loopy, playmate for Daisy. 'He's my boy,' she says, 'my best friend.' He certainly helped heal some of our hurt. We were still persisting with fertility treatment, and miserable as hell with the perpetual ups and downs of it, but trying desperately not to lean on the outside world or to let it impede on what were, after all, Daisy's days. But something was changing.

It had become slowly clear that it was not the pregnancy we craved but a bigger family. This realisation for us was not a revolutionary moment, but a chain of feelings that had slowly linked together and were finally joined by the saddest moment of our lives to date.

We'd been waiting for news of my friends' first baby, and it was while we were getting up one morning, chatting excitedly with Daisy about the imminent new arrival, and getting her ready, that the phone rang. James answered it. Our friends' baby, a boy, had died during labour. All that expectation, all those hopes and dreams had gone in a devastating instant. Daisy sat on the sofa, quiet, staring at us while James and I just looked at one another. Tears streamed down my face, and I remember repeating, 'Oh my god, oh my god, oh my god.' We pulled ourselves together, attempted to explain it to Daisy without understanding it ourselves, and then ushered the poor child off to nursery school. The rest is not my story to tell.

The little boy's death did not change the way I felt. It did underline what I already knew and was instrumental in moving us forward. I believe to this day that you do not have to have seen your children to love them. I loved Daisy while she grew inside me, and Tom from the moment I heard about him. It is the first day at school, the cuddles, the little things that children say that make you laugh so heartily when they are finally, thankfully, in bed asleep, that we longed to repeat with our second child, not the biological link. It was James, interestingly enough, who made the call to stop the fertility treatment. We were reclaiming our lives. Enough was enough. Adoption was to be our choice, our option. We would set off down that road and see where our journey took us. We felt free at last and giddy with the power of decision.

Cue to the chat with Daisy. More of a fluffy chicks and buzzy bumblebees type of chat, suitable for four-year-olds, than the birds and bees one itself. I put all those jolly pregnant people we met to good use as case studies to show how, although all babies grow inside their mummy's tummy, not all the mummies are able to look after their children. 'Why?' was the inevitable question. 'Because...' I started thinking of all the material I had read, of the statistics, the facts and heart-wrenchingly gritty stories, 'because they might be too poorly or unhappy,' I continued, watching her every movement, thinking all the time of that proverbial can of worms. Daisy played coyly on the lounge floor, a question clearly forming. I decided to move quickly on to the point in hand rather than brave the wriggly worms.

'These children need new mummies and daddies.' I paused, wondering what her reaction, so absolutely crucial to us, would be. 'And most definitely new bossy big sisters,' I added. I saw her eyes flicker in recognition and so went for broke: 'Daddy and I were thinking that maybe we should give one of these children a home. That maybe we could be their new mummy and daddy and that you could be their big sister.'

Daisy is not the easiest girl to second-guess. She was still preoccupied with the startling fact that there were children out there without parents. When she realised we could do something about it, she turned round, matter of fact, and said: 'That's what we must do then,' quite obviously incredulous that we hadn't thought of it sooner.

She did, however, have strict criteria: that they were to be younger and shorter than her and unable to do cartwheels. Over the time it took to get through the process, a mind blowing three years from beginning to end, Daisy's criteria changed to: a younger brother to make stink bombs with.

And so Daisy proudly announced our decision at the dinner table in her best friend's house, whose parents were privy to the news. 'We're adopting!' Her best friend, Holly, was mightily impressed, 'Wow, really?!' to which Daisy excitedly replied, 'Seriously!' Her beloved best friend then very politely, so as not to spoil the moment, asked, 'What's adopting?'

From *When Daisy met Tommy*, by Jules Belle, published by BAAF in 2010 (pp 7–10). © Jules Belle

ON CONSIDERING ADOPTION

What was missing in my life

It was following this trauma and with a new sense of my own strength of character that I started to look at my life and see the holes. After the operation I had three months to convalesce, during which time I watched a lot of TV. Hours and hours of watching fairly pointless and completely forgettable television was enough to make me wonder at the futility of the hours and hours of my life I spent making fairly pointless and completely forgettable television programmes, often with some rather unpleasant people. When I was well, I went back to work reluctantly and started to look for ways to improve my life. I looked ahead and realised that if I didn't do something I would end up miserable and alone. I began to realise that what was missing in my life was a family – children. Then I discovered, quite by chance, that I might be able to adopt a child on my own. I knew that I was in a position financially to set myself up so that I would at least be able to make ends meet for a few years. I thought it through. I made a choice and happily my joyful child reminds me daily that it was the right choice, not only for me, but also for him.

From *Flying Solo*, by Julia Wise, published by BAAF in 2007 (p 6). © Julia Wise

Why did we make that phone call?

We made our first phone call to the adoption society about seven years ago. At that time our three birth children, Ed, Kate and Robbie, were aged thirteen, eleven and ten. Life was good. We didn't *need* any more children. We certainly didn't plan to have any more birth children; Evie had had the operation! If you pause to think about it, why does anyone want children anyway, whether through birth or adoption? Parents sacrifice careers, nights out, holidays, material things, freedom and so on, in return for years of thankless exhaustion. It probably has its roots in an instinctive drive to keep the species going, to preserve the family name, and an innate need to be needed. Our lives would have been emptier, I think, if we had not had the joy and angst of helping our children grow up, from the earliest stages of utter dependency after the cutting of the actual umbilical cord, to the gradual severing of the metaphorical cord as they approach adulthood. Not that it ever gets completely cut, of course. Parenthood is a lifelong life choice for those lucky enough to be able to make it. But it's not what everyone wants, which is fine, and for some it is unlooked for.

We lived, and still do, in a small Scottish town, and as our three children were getting older, my wife, Evie, and I were beginning to have a bit more time to ourselves. Not that life has ever been quiet: my work as a social worker, and Evie's job as a community development worker and volunteer means that, for as long as I can remember, we've always had a backlog of cleaning, decorating, gardening, and piles of unsorted papers spilling out from various dusty corners, which we call "the in-tray". We'll catch up one day: one evening or one weekend, or one holiday or maybe when we retire. Or maybe we won't ever catch up: life's too short to fritter it away on hoovering!

So why did we make that phone call? And why did we make it then, seven years ago, when life was getting a bit easier? It wasn't just so that we could continue to have an excuse for not doing the hoovering! As anyone who has been through an adoption assessment process knows, the hoover gets used more before the social worker's visits than ever before. The reasons are difficult to explain, and probably impossible for anyone else to understand, but I think we made the call when we did, precisely because life was good. We were sitting in the garden one sunny spring weekend; the grass had been cut, the sparrows hopped and chattered, sunshine spilled and moved across the distant hills, and the freshly ground coffee was perfect. After a fairly short conversation, we agreed that I would phone the adoption society on the Monday. Our three children were all out and the house was very quiet. We were surprisingly decisive.

Evie and I had talked about adoption for years as something we might do some day. The seed of the idea had lain dormant, but like something stored in a matchbox, we took it out and re-examined it periodically. In my work I was involved in planning for children in need of adoption, and was aware that some would never get families; mostly older children with traumatic histories, sibling groups and children with additional needs and disabilities. I regularly saw adoption magazines, with pages and pages of groomed, smiling children, coaxed into appealing poses by professional photographers, to catch the eye of would-be families, with positively spun captions underneath:

Alfie has had lots of changes in his life. He has a cheeky personality and needs lots of patience and firm boundaries.

Being in the business, I knew that probably meant a history of abuse, attachment disorder and ADHD (Attention Deficit Hyperactive Disorder). Half-jokingly at first, I'd spoken with Evie about how instead of spending our working lives shuffling bits of paper around, we'd be better doing something that would make a real difference, but we didn't do anything other than talk about it till after that sunny weekend.

* * *

The decision to adopt, or even to make that first phone call, isn't at all straightforward. It's the beginning of an unknown journey. I've always been a slightly nervous traveller. I like to know exactly what the arrangements are and to get to the airport in plenty of time. But the adoption journey is more of a mystery tour. There was no child in mind when we embarked on the process. It's a bit like deciding to get married without having a specific partner in mind. Of course, having a birth child is also like that, but the birth child grows out of you, and you make that skin-to-skin contact in the first few moments. An adopted child already has a name, has come from the union of others and has a personality and a will that is partly formed. He or she might have had that special skin-to-skin contact with someone else, if they were lucky.

We thought a lot about the sort of child that would fit in best with our family. We felt there needed to be a substantial age gap between Robbie and the newcomer, so as to avoid too much rivalry and minimise the risk of Robbie feeling displaced. We planned that the new child would share a room with Robbie. We had a little box room, which was used as a "study"; in other words, we kept our "in tray" and miscellaneous junk in it. If possible we wanted to hang on to it – but it could always be used as a bedroom if the need arose. We were wary of taking on a child with acute attachment difficulties, or one with overt sexualised behaviour, because of our protectiveness towards the others.

We ended up thinking that a child with mild disabilities might be the best fit: perhaps a child with Down's syndrome or a limited physical disability. We'd each done a bit of voluntary work with disabled children in the past, and had provided a little bit of care to the disabled child of some friends. The summer before, Evie had met a man at the Great Yorkshire Show who, along with his wife, had adopted four children with Down's syndrome, all adults by then. Two of them were with him. Evie got chatting – she comes from a long line of chatterers – and came away inspired at the man's life choice and the richness that had followed for him and his wife and children. All these little experiences added up and influenced the way we would go.

Of course, the term "mild disability" is a bit elastic. As a prospective birth parent your first thought at the birth is whether the baby is okay. As an actual parent you never know what lies ahead: there's the possibility of impaired health or development; the spectre of your children being drawn to drugs, drink, getting into trouble or into relationships that worry you. If disabilities are detected at birth, there's the added uncertainty of how independent or otherwise children might become. In the case of William, whom we adopted, a major concern was whether or not he would be able to walk. He's ten years old now, and we think the answer is no. But the prospects were brighter when he was placed with us.

Then there was the question as to whether we should foster or adopt. We never really considered fostering. We both felt that if children didn't have a birth family they could stay with for ever, then adoption was the next best thing, and that we were most likely to make a real difference to a child if we committed wholly through adoption. Having said that, there are many children with disabilities who do very well in long-term foster placements, and of course for children who have significant contact with their birth families, that is often the preferred option. We'd talked to the other children before that first phone call. We were always clear we could not go ahead without their support.

We'd talked in general terms about children who needed families, and engendered some excitement and enthusiasm, which we hoped would not be disappointed. We kept stressing that it might not happen; that we might decide not to go ahead; that we might not be approved and so on. But a momentum developed after that first phone call that led to William joining our family a few months later.

Extracts from *The Family Business*, by Robert Marsden, published by BAAF in 2008 (pp 12–15 and pp 17–19).
© Robert Marsden

Why do it?

We got married in Spain in May 2007 (same-sex marriages – as opposed to civil partnerships – became legal in Spain in 2005). After the wedding we started talking about adoption a bit more seriously again. In the end we reached the conclusion that there was never going to be a time when we were both 100 per cent sure that adoption was the right thing for us. The uncertainties and changing factors are so many that it would be impossible. The difference this time was that instead of just letting the matter drop for another few months as we'd done before, we decided that we would do something about it. Make enquiries, start the application process, even get approved by a panel...all those things don't mean that you have to take a child on if you are not sure. We could always stop the process if we changed our minds.

So why do it? We must be such traditional guys that a few months after getting married we've started going on about having children! I suppose it's quite a natural thing to do. You get to that age in your mid-thirties when all your (heterosexual) friends have children. I always wanted to have children. Then I accepted that I was gay and thought that it was not to be, which to me was one of the hardest things about coming out.

But the more I thought about it, the more I realised that this needn't be the case. I love children. I love playing with my friends' kids and with my nephew and nieces. It feels quite natural to me. It's what people do, isn't it? They have children. I don't see why I shouldn't have a paternal instinct just because I'm gay. I want to look after a child (or children). I want to bring them up, educate them, watch them grow, support them, share their joy in the good times and cry with them in the bad times. I want to be a grandfather one day (but not too soon!). I know Mike and I would make good parents.

Mike struggles with this still. He worries that we'll get the child from hell who will burn the house down on the first day. More importantly, he worries that because we're a gay couple, we'll be imposing something on the children that will make them stand out: they'll get called names at school, get picked on. I tell him that they'll probably get picked on anyway. They could have big ears, or red hair, or whatever else you get picked on at school for. And whilst coming home to two dads may not be the ideal family they are dreaming of as they sit in a foster home waiting to be adopted, surely it has to beat not being adopted at all.

We know there will be intrusions and difficult moments. That it will be hard, and emotional, full of doubts and life-changing, whatever the outcome. We'll find out a lot about ourselves. We'll have to make tough decisions. We also know that we'll have doubts and change our minds back and forth a million times. But that is the process we are starting; and maybe at the end of it there will be more than two of us in our family.

Reproduced from *Becoming Dads*, by Pablo Fernández, published by BAAF in 2011 (pp 2–4). © Pablo Fernández

We are framily!

On a bright Sunday morning in autumn, 19 people gather in the living room of Louise and Rick, the proud adoptive parents of Katie, aged two. It isn't a very large living room, but there are enough comfortable chairs and sofas for everyone to get up close and, of course, the nine children in the group prefer sitting on the floor. These are the people who make up Katie's network, and it is not at all unusual for them to get together in this way, but on this occasion they have gathered to tell their story.

The story begins long before Katie was adopted. Both sets of grandparents belong to this group; the others are Louise's and Rick's lifelong friends and their children – three of them already grown up. Some of the adults have known each other since they were infants and all the children consider themselves like "cousins at least", as one of them said. Louise and Rick are godparents to some of them and special auntie and uncle to all of them, because until Katie arrived they were the only childless couple in the group with more time to spare for special activities and treats. But in fact all the women have always been "the aunties" for each other's children and now they are Katie's.

There is nothing formal or organised about this group: they all get together for special events, some families share holidays, the "aunties" regularly meet in pairs or trios or quartets: 'It feels like a sisterhood among the girls.' Some members live close to each other and see each other daily, they all support each other, listen to each other's stories and look out for each other's children. And the children are happy to spend time with their "aunties" without their own parents being there.

All the members of the group know each other well enough to draw on each other's strengths and offer advice only when it is needed. *We have learned when to give advice and when not to, when to speak and when to hold our tongue.* They call themselves the "framily": a group made up of family and friends. They have created a virtual village in defiance of modern life.

When Louise and Rick decided to adopt, the group was with them every step of the long, emotional journey that lasted four years from the time of the initial application to being matched with Katie.

Louise and Rick shared the adoption process with the group. Everyone understood what was happening. Long before Katie was even born, the children did a "Build a Bear" workshop and made a bear for the new child-to-be, which they all signed. Two of the women attended a Family and Friends training day offered regularly by the local authority working with Louise and Rick. They found it really helpful as it threw up issues they hadn't thought of, and they could share what they had learned with the wider group to ensure that the adopting couple had the best possible support around them. Both sets of parents, now Katie's grandparents, and two other members of the group were referees.

After Louise and Rick were approved to adopt, everyone expected a child to be placed with them fairly quickly. After all, this was to be a third generation adoption: Louise was adopted and so was her father – no problem.

But third time round it took another two years. During that period there were several disappointments, with five links not progressing to a viable match. It was a stressful time. Louise said that it felt like having five miscarriages in a row. The waiting was hard on the network children. Each of them had been prepared to expect another child and they became impatient and couldn't understand why it was taking so long. It was hard for the adults too, especially for the grandparents-in-waiting, to see the couple go through so much pain and disappointment and to feel powerless to help them. There seemed to be no reason for such a long delay. They were all aware of the growing tensions and were careful not to dwell on the subject of adoption unless Louise and Rick raised it, and they tried to get on with doing fun things together.

Louise relied heavily on the group while she and Rick bore each disappointment and waited for a child, but at the same time they agreed not to discuss any more potential links with the network until there was a definite match. So when Katie was mentioned to them, they didn't speak about her until they had met with her social worker and her foster carer and knew that they were the only adopters being considered for Katie.

When they knew Katie was finally coming to live with Auntie Louise and Uncle Rick, some of the children were concerned that their own relationship with them would change and that they might not see them as much, or be loved as much. They were assured that 'There is definitely enough love to go round'. And Katie quickly became the adored youngest member of the "framily".

When Katie arrived, aged six months, everyone met her individually in her new home – grandparents first. She wasn't "passed around" or overwhelmed by the whole group; the "framily" respected that she had first to feel safe being held by her new parents, that she had to get used slowly to her new environment and that they shouldn't ask too many questions about Katie's past. They knew that Louise and Rick would share what they could, and what was appropriate, when they felt ready. Everyone in the network is careful about what they say to other people and respect the fact that 'The people outside the network, who don't know the background, don't need to know'. They stress the difference between secrecy and privacy; when asked, the children say that Katie is their cousin. Ruby, aged 14, explains: 'It's her information, not ours, and one day Katie can decide whether to say she's adopted.'

From *Related by Adoption*, by Hedi Argent (3rd edition), published by BAAF in 2014 (pp 58–61). © Hedi Argent

Preparing for child care experience

....
....
....
....
....
....
....
....
....
....
....
....
....
....
....
....
....
....
....
....
....
....
....
....

What do you need to be an adoptive parent?

....
....
....
....
....
....
....
....
....
....
....
....
....
....
....
....
....
....
....
....
....
....

Having a child will change your life

Consider the psychological, social, emotional and practical impacts on your life. Note down some of these below.

- Your relationship with your partner (if you have one)

....

....

....

- Your relationship with your wider family

....

....

....

- Your relationships with your friends

....

....

....

- Your job

....

....

....

- Your social life

....

....

....

- Your home and garden

....

....

....

- Your spare time and hobbies and interests

....

....

....

Preparing for a child moving in

MODULE 7: **Linking, matching and introductions**

Learning outcomes

This module aims to help you to:

- **understand how adopters are linked and matched with a child or children**
- **understand the process of preparing children for adoption**
- **know what to expect in terms of meeting your child(ren) and having your child(ren) move in**
- **consider how you can help your child(ren) to settle in**
- **consider how to support children's identity needs**

ON LINKING AND MATCHING

One of the most far-reaching decisions social workers make is the selection of a new permanent family for a child in care. What power we wield when we artificially create families and relationships – the responsibility is mind-boggling. And yet, bizarrely, these giant steps taken on behalf of vulnerable people are based on minimal evidence:

...there is no substantive research about matching of children and families, and there are many different opinions about what is important.

(Triseliotis *et al*, 1997, p 157)

– and then, over a decade later:

...in comparison with associated topics such as recruitment, assessment, preparation, introductions and post-placement support, the literature on matching per se is extremely scant. This is somewhat surprising given the importance of the complex matching process that needs to take place. Placing children, many of whom have complex needs, with an unrelated adoptive family is one of the most important decisions in child care. It is also potentially one of the most difficult.

(Dance *et al*, 2010, p 14)

Historically, matching seems to have been a much easier task. The stigma of adoption up to the last quarter of the 20th century, now much reduced, meant that the main intention of any match was to disguise the lack of a blood-tie between infant (the children for adoption *were* mostly infants) and new parents. Physical resemblance was therefore a key criterion – maybe the foremost. Given that babies' skin and hair colour can change during development, and that biological parents' appearance is not necessarily a reliable indicator, this was a somewhat hit and miss methodology. Nowadays, matching practice tends to rely on the lessons from adoptions which disrupt or break down, and more generally from "outcomes", to the point where we tend to know more about what goes wrong than why things go right (Quinton *et al*, 1998; Dance and Rushton, 2005; Argent and Coleman, 2006). We therefore tend to base our judgments in the matching process on the risk factors which should be avoided rather than the positives which should be sought. We should also approach our matching efforts with some degree of humility: at least one commentator argues that it is what happens *during* a placement (particularly the quality of the support) which matters more than the preceding processes, including matching (Russell, 2006).

In the absence of clear predictors of matching success, the suggestions in this book should be taken as food for thought rather than determining guidelines. We cannot create long-lasting families through an Excel spreadsheet. In fact, in the realm of human relationships, flexibility is important, so that room is allowed for that magical ingredient: "chemistry". Whether this is based on recognition of difference or similarity, or is stubbornly indefinable remains a moot point. Sometimes we have to accept that chemistry defies known wisdom and the most apparently unlikely matches work well.

In order to clarify the parameters of this book, a distinction is drawn between linking and matching. These terms were once used interchangeably but it is more helpful to name them as distinctive processes:

- **The link** can be described as the initial step in thinking that this family may be suitable for this child: the point when, out of all the families and all the children, the two halves are first placed side by side.

Links can be achieved through one of two different methods: either through social workers cross-matching data about the child and potential families, or through families themselves responding to information about children (profiles, photographs, videos/DVDs – even through face-to-face meetings in specially arranged "placement parties").

The first method (using social workers as brokers) need not be as mechanical as it sounds: often, as Triseliotis *et al* point out (1997), the most suitable "kind" of child emerges during the long process of the adults' preparation and assessment, and the social workers (who in some agencies know the waiting children) may already see potential links even before more formal methods, such as Adoption Registers, become necessary.

The second method of linking was first highlighted by Cousins (2003) who described it as "child-led" (because it uses the direct appeal of the child), though more recently it has been dubbed adopter-led, which acknowledges that the prospective carers, rather than social work staff, are in the driving seat. Essentially, using this method, the link suggests itself through a response to the child by the adults – often through publications such as *Be My Parent* or *Children Who Wait*. Some of these adults have not at this stage even applied to an agency and may be taken up and assessed with this child in mind (though under England regulations, any subsequent approval would be generic). With this method, social workers stand back and allow chemistry to play its part. Their skills come in at the next stage – the match.

- **The match** can be described as the outcome of a considered assessment of the potential link by social work staff and eventually the panel and the agency decision-maker. It is a conclusion reached that *this* child and *this* family are indeed suited to each other, and that the connection should be formalised. The process of assessing the compatibility of the two parties involves a careful exploration of whether the child's needs could be met by these carers; whether the family's needs could be met by the child; and what supports might be necessary to ensure a long-lasting relationship. No one should doubt the complexity of this process, or the skills required.

Reproduced from *Ten Top Tips for Making Matches*, by Jennifer Cousins, published by BAAF in 2011 (pp 1–4). © BAAF

Process for identifying a family after a decision that a child should be placed for adoption

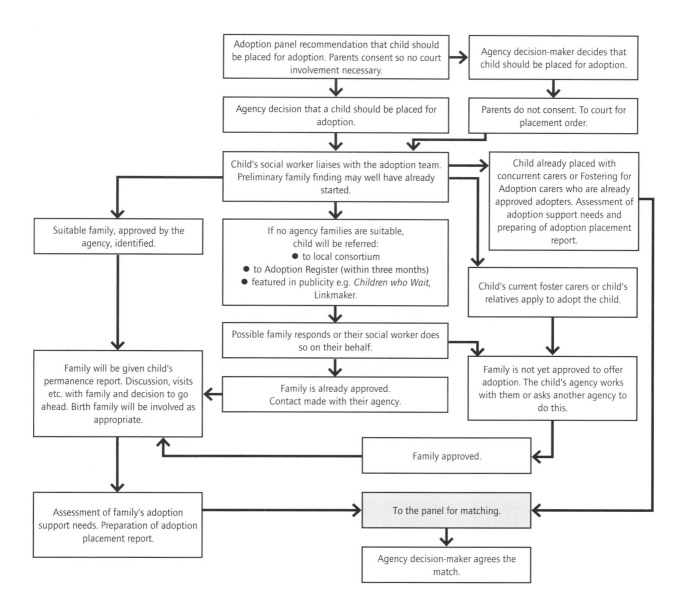

ON INTRODUCTIONS

Introductions for children of different ages

Babies 0–18 months

- They cannot understand change – they can only "feel" it

- May experience loss of usual carers as total abandonment and be distressed
- Implications for introductions

Implications for introductions

- Create familiar sensory experiences, i.e. how things look, smell and feel.
- Keep the baby in the same routine as in the foster home – there will be plenty of time to make gradual changes later. Adopters should understand that "tuning in" to the child's needs will promote strong attachments far more quickly than trying to impose unfamiliar routines.
- Use the same washing powder so that bedding and clothing feel and smell the same.
- Keep the foster carers in the picture as much as possible; an infant will not understand the reasons for sudden separation.
- Allow the child to grieve while offering comfort.

Children 18 months–3 years

- May regress to earlier behaviours, e.g. toilet-training, eating, sleep patterns, getting upset easily
- Adopters should retain established routines
- Familiar objects, bedding, favourite toys and clothes will ease transition

Children 3–5 years

- Find new situations threatening
- Change may trigger memories of earlier moves
- Often very interested in books, DVDs, provided by the prospective adopters
- May be able to follow a simple calendar outlining waiting time and/or what will happen on each day of introductions
- Foster carer can reassure the child, help adopters learn about the child

Children 5–10 years

- May feel anxious about hurting their present carers or birth family members
- Foster carers may have ambivalent feelings if bonds are close – glad but sad
- They may need to show the child that he/she has "permission" to form new attachments

Introductions for children with disabilities

- Adopters will need time to feel confident caring for the child's medical and physical needs
- Important to meet with consultants, specialists where possible
- Special considerations for a child with sensory disabilities meeting new parent(s)

Introductions and placement for siblings

- Some sibling groups may have been living in separate foster homes
- Adopters are usually introduced to all the siblings together
- The plan may specify time to get to know each child individually
- Placing at the same time or consecutively? There is no single "right" way

- They can be placed together even if fostered separately
- If children have depended on one another for support, separating them may cause distress
- Consecutive placements can be helpful in some cases

The best feeling ever

There are days of your life you will never forget. I may have had more than my fair share already, but 2 September 2009 is out in front for me now. That's the day we met our son.

Following the decision to place him with us, there has been all the usual red tape to deal with: meetings with the medical adviser and his current foster carers; a placement planning meeting; more forms to fill in for the Panel that will be asked to recommend the match; and of course attending the Panel itself.

It has all taken time, but everything has gone without a hitch. After the Matching Panel, we agreed the final details of our "introductions" plan – the eight-day period that would bridge our first meeting with our child and the day our beautiful baby boy would join our family. And if that first meeting was special, it is hard to put into words what today means to us both. Today we get to take him home and we become Mum and Dad at last. It's a wonderful if daunting prospect.

During the introductions we have spent hours at the foster carers' house with our little boy. They have even brought him over to our house on a couple of days and he has spent quite a bit of time with us in his new home. It's all about making the transition as painless and natural as possible for all of us. And that includes his foster carers and the rest of their family, who must all be going through seven shades of hell at the prospect of losing him so soon. Which will be in about an hour or so, I reckon, as this is all it will take us to drive to their house and pick him up.

We arrive at the foster carers' house and everything happens very fast. There are tears on all sides. Even the social workers present are struggling to contain their emotions. For almost the first time in my life I turn down the offer of a cup of tea. This has to be done quickly, for everyone's sake, and before we know it the most precious cargo we have ever carried is loaded into the car and we are on our way.

I pull off their drive and if I have ever driven more slowly and more carefully, I don't remember the time. The road stretches out in front of us as we head home with our little boy safely on board. It's a couple of minutes before I realise I am holding my breath. I let out a big sigh and think of all the test tubes, the frozen embryos and the doctors; all the meetings, the forms and the social workers. The ups and the downs this journey has taken us on.

Suddenly none of that matters any more – we have the most amazing son and it's the best feeling ever. I sneak a look at the little chap when we pull up at a traffic light. He has nodded off and gurgles lightly in his sleep. We still have a few more social worker visits to get through, a couple of formal reviews to attend and the legal adoption to complete the deal. Then there are all the joys and the heartaches our new lives will bring. Everything that's gone and everything that's still to come – I know it's all been (and will be!) worth it. The proof of that is in the back of the car today. And, whatever the future holds for all three of us, we are a family now and we don't feel cold any more.

ON SUPPORTING CHILDREN AND IDENTITY NEEDS

Why do life story work?

Children who live with their birth families have the opportunity to know about their past, and have a means of being able to understand it through discussions with their parents and others and to clarify past events in terms of the present. Children separated from their birth families are often denied this opportunity; they may have changed families, social workers, homes and neighbourhoods. Their past may be lost, much of it even forgotten.

When children lose track of their past, they may well find it difficult to develop emotionally and socially. If adults cannot or do not discuss this past with them, it is reasonable for children to suppose that it may be bad.

What is life story work?

Life story work is an attempt to give back some of this past to children separated from their family of origin. Gathering together facts about that life and the significant people in it helps them begin to accept their past and go forward into the future with this knowledge. We have found that most children separated in this way gain a great deal from talking about their past, present and future to a sympathetic adult. Life story work provides a structure for talking to children. In fact, everyone can gain benefits from such a process – children and adults. Interesting work has been carried out by social workers with adults (an example is mentioned in the booklist) who need to experience attention-giving and be given help in orientating themselves. Similarly, elderly people get a great deal from "reminiscence therapy", and Age Concern have produced a very helpful pack for work with groups of people, illustrating the power of nostalgia and affirming people's sense of identity.

Children separated from their birth parents, whether they are in a residential unit, with foster carers, or going to a permanent new family or returning to their birth family, need to sort out why the separation occurred and why various adults have been unable to care for them. We have often failed in the past to give the children for whom we have been responsible the opportunity to do this. Our experience with the children whom we have worked with has encouraged us to believe that life story work is a useful way of fulfilling this need, and that all the children have benefited in some way.

Life story work may result in a book or video, an audio tape or a computer file, or simply be a record of sessions which took place. It does not *have* to result in a product – it is the process rather than just the product which will yield most benefits for the children and young people involved; the product will be the "record".

All children are entitled to an accurate knowledge of their past and their family. This is a right that children who are secure in their families take for granted. For those children separated from their birth families, the right to this knowledge is equally important, not only for the sake of the children themselves, but also for their own children.

Life story work can usefully be adapted, not only to suit elderly people, but also the parents from whom children are separated. Many parents, whose children are currently being looked after, have been in the care system themselves. The possibility of someone having done life story work with them is remote. However, if it is carried out with them as adults, it may help clarify the reasons, for both children and parents, for the family not being able to live together, and in so doing make best use of the separation.

The Adoption and Children Act 2002 (England and Wales) lays renewed stress on the need for children to be involved in discussions that affect their lives. Life story work can be a means of giving the child age-appropriate information that allows them to make these informed decisions. For example, the child who discloses the identity of an adult in the birth family home who has sexually abused him or her will need to understand that it may not be possible to return home while this situation prevails.

Life story work should complement the underlying philosophy of the Adoption and Children Act 2002 – of participation and involvement of the child and his or her family.

What do children get from life story work?

Life story work gives children a structured and understandable way of talking about themselves. It can produce clarity where there are dangerous or idealised fantasies. Once completed, it provides them with a record which they and, with their agreement, the adults caring for them can refer to at any time, particularly when there is a crisis.

Life story work can increase a child's sense of self-worth and self-esteem because, sadly, at the back of the minds of nearly all children separated from their families of origin is the thought that they are worthless and unlovable. They blame themselves for the actions of adults. If they have been abandoned, neglected or injured by their parents or other family members, they are convinced that they brought it upon themselves.

Another aspect of this feeling is described by Kate Cairns (*Attachment, Trauma and Resilience*, BAAF, 2002) who reports that some children feel so intrinsically "bad" that they feel that talking about themselves may "contaminate" other people. You, the worker, need to make it clear to the child that *you* are the adult and can cope with the child's expressions of emotion connected with trauma and pain.

Life story work provides an opportunity to show children why they should be proud of themselves, and this positive attitude should be evident in any book, video or other record, which results. In talking about their birth parents, for example, although you may tell them a suitably-worded version of the truth (however painful that may be) about their family and why they are being looked after, it is important to stress the positive side. You need to talk about their birth parents in non-judgemental terms. Perhaps you might say that not everybody is good at being a parent, but that does not mean they are bad in other respects.

Preparing to adopt – loving and losing, and keeping family links alive

When you have worked together on a child's life story, you will feel much closer to the child. We have found that memories of our own childhoods are always awoken. If we, too, have experienced pain, we share this with the child – while always remembering whose story it is! Some people do life story work with more than one child at a time, and some sharing of experiences – without breaking confidences, of course – can make a child feel better. Thus a child can appreciate that many people experience pain in their childhood and that the fault does not lie with them; they need not feel guilt or responsibility, as so many children amazingly do, for their parents' behaviour.

Finally, you and the child need to be able to relax and enjoy at least some parts of each of the sessions and, for this, you may need to re-learn how to play. This is a chance to have a lot of fun! With some of the play techniques suggested later on, you will need to get down on the floor with the child and play with toys. Self-consciousness is not a virtue in this situation but, if you need a reason, you should know that your playing has a serious purpose and is a valuable technique, and is as important as being able to talk naturally to a child about important issues. While not all life story work will lead you into play, some will and you might as well enjoy yourself while you are playing!

Reproduced from *Life Story Work*, by Tony Ryan and Rodger Walker (3rd edition), published by BAAF in 2007 (pp 3–5). This clear and practical guide explains the importance of life story work, and presents a wide assortment of useful techniques and exercises for anyone doing life story work with children. © Tony Ryan and Rodger Walker

Sharing memories

William is one of six birth children. The information we have about most of the others is frozen in time, in the photographs and captions in his life story book. There are a few photographs of his mother, holding William on her lap during visits to the children's centre, accompanied by her two older children. In one picture she's cradling him in her arms and smiling down at him. They're family snaps, and without the full story could be of any family, caught at random, doing nothing in particular. There's a picture of William's eldest brother holding him, and of the next one leaning over and grinning. They seem nice boys. At times William longs for them, though he can have no memory of them; he hasn't seen them since he was two. There are three other younger brothers; two have been adopted together and another, the youngest, is still at home, and we don't have any photos of him. They all have the same father, and they all have a similar look about them. The photographs are over six years old and we have no information about what has become of William's birth family since the pictures were taken. We can't answer his questions about them. It's hard for him to picture the older ones as different from the way they appear on the glossy, slippery photos that catch little patches of white electric light as he looks at them. They will be teenagers now: young adults beginning to make their own way somehow. I sometimes wonder how we would all get on if we met. It's an odd feeling to know that your son has brothers out there somewhere, who might or might not be in need, and with whom you have a connection that is difficult to define.

Occasionally William can be preoccupied with his life story book for days on end. It was beginning to feel quite morbid, so we put together an album of his early years in our family, so that he can look back with positive nostalgia and we can share common memories. It seems to have helped.

From *The Family Business*, by Robert Marsden, published by BAAF in 2008 (p 67). © Robert Marsden

ON FIRST MEETINGS

We will finally be a family

Friday 25 July 2003

Peter's Form E arrives on a gloriously sunny morning – a good omen, we feel. We rush to open it and Robbie takes a quick look before leaving for work. Then I read it thoroughly from start to finish.

Before long I am ringing Rob at work to discuss various points of interest in the form. There is nothing in the detailed report that either of us finds troubling – Peter sounds like a normal, playful, stubborn, mischievous and lovable little boy. He sounds like our son.

We are also thrilled that he is still comparatively young – turning three in a few months, in late autumn. We ring Tim to confirm that we wish to proceed. Things then move so fast that it all becomes a bit of a blur. Within hours Tim is ringing us back to tell us that Peter's social worker, Clare, would like to come down to meet us the following Thursday. As this means a three hour drive, we figure she must really like the sound of us!

We are so excited all over again, as is my mother who has remained quietly optimistic throughout and comforted me whenever I have nearly felt like giving up. Is our son really waiting for us out there? Peter, can you ever begin to realise how much we want you to be part of our family?

We start to believe that our luck is really about to change. Dare we allow ourselves to think so positively while perhaps heading for yet another fall? It is certainly difficult to stay composed at such a time, and we cannot help but build our hopes up once again.

Thursday 31 July 2003

Then, before we know it, the following Thursday is upon us. We are both stressed – more so than at our ill-fated meeting, some two weeks earlier. That meeting has left a nasty taste in our mouths and we are desperate not to let anything cloud our view of Clare when she arrives. Tim, as usual, arrives forty-five minutes early. We talk through various pointers regarding Peter and I prepare some lunch for us all, knowing that Clare will be here around midday, after a long drive. Only ten minutes later than scheduled, Clare arrives – and immediately she appears friendly and easy to talk to. Our first impression is a good one.

The meeting lasts about three hours altogether and it is a very, very different experience from the previous one. Clare talks animatedly about Peter, making him "come alive". She answers all of our questions and asks us many more, without ever making us feel that we are being unduly judged or interrogated. She seems to love our dogs, likes the house very much and she really seems to like us. She is very, very positive, even talking to Tim about arranging the next meeting to include the foster carer.

The only blot on the horizon is the fact that we are not the only family being considered for Peter after all. His details have been sent to another family who live only fifteen miles away from where he presently lives with his foster carer. Our hearts sink. Even though Clare seems extremely disinterested in visiting this other family, we know from experience that it is foolish to be too confident. Nonetheless, when Clare asks if we would like to see Peter's life story book, we both say "yes". We have decided that we definitely want to see a picture of this little boy who might become our son, and the life story book turns out to be a revelation.

There is Peter's birth certificate, his first romper suit, first baby photos, pictures of birth mum and grandma, and letters from previous foster carers. It is a potted history of Peter's life and we feel privileged to be allowed to share in it. But it makes us think that if we do end up losing this child as well as Annie, then we might have to give up. Once you see photos of a child – a beaming face, a glimpse into their personality – you are deeply involved already.

Peter, seeing your shock of auburn hair and huge green eyes, you could so easily be our biological son. We so want to meet you, so want to have the chance to take care of you.

And I do not know yet whether we will be given that chance. Robbie says to me later that evening, 'Clare must be pretty sure of us to show us Peter's life story work. Otherwise, it would be just too cruel a thing to do.'

Friday 1 August 2003

The very next day Tim rings to update us. He has heard from Clare, and she very much wants to proceed with Rob and me. As far as she is concerned, the other family lives too close to Peter's birth family and she thinks it is imperative that Peter lives some distance away from his home town. Everything is looking very good indeed. Clare will run things past her manager the following Monday or Tuesday, and then we will have a final decision.

Who would have believed it? Only a couple of weeks earlier we were in the depths of despair. Our families, friends, and indeed our social worker, were all at a loss as to what to say to us. And now just look at us! But I have to say again just how hard the waiting becomes – and we have had to wait a short time compared to many other adopters we know. But only a matter of days can stretch into an agonising length of time. You try to keep busy and endeavour to fill your mind with something else, but it is quite impossible. Impossible when the decision could be life-changing.

Monday 4 August 2003

Tim rings us on the Monday afternoon to tell us that he hasn't heard anything yet. He himself is tense and says he cannot begin to imagine how Rob and I must be feeling. We are like coiled springs, in fact. All our family and friends have been glued to their phones for the entire week, and the tension is mounting. My parents are almost tying themselves in knots with the anxiety, and desperately trying to remain positive. Rob's mum is almost too scared to ring – wanting to know while not wanting to bombard us with questions.

Wednesday 6 August 2003

Robbie and I are beginning to feel physically ill – we just cannot understand what is holding things up. Tim has spoken to Clare and she has assured him that everything is fine. She has decided not to assess the other family and wants to recommend only us. She tells us that she is merely waiting to have the "official" approval from her boss. Her manager is on leave and she has to apply to the Head of the Adoption Services to get the go ahead. This, it seems, is taking time.

Thursday 7 August 2003

Finally, at lunchtime, the phone call comes. It is Tim; he congratulates us on becoming parents at last. Clare has emailed him to say that it has all been made official. She is delighted to tell us that Peter is to be our son! On hearing the news I literally scream down the phone. Tim is happy for us both and is not in the least bit surprised when I start crying.

My friend, Janeen, is here when the news comes, having called round for lunch with her little boy. I am truly grateful that she is with me as I soon become quite emotional with the enormity of it all. For almost nine years Rob and I have waited for the moment when we can say that we are going to be parents. Now, at long last, that moment is here. For me it is like seeing the blue line on a pregnancy test for the very first time. Nothing else compares.

I phone Robbie at work and tell him the good news. He is overjoyed, of course, and comes home early and we start ringing round everyone we know. We are particularly touched by the response of our nephew and niece, Luke and Bethany, aged nine and four. They have taken a great interest all the way along and have waited patiently for news, sometimes thinking that it was never going to happen! They are excited when we tell them that we are going to have a son. Especially Bethany when she realises that her new cousin will be so close to her in age. She asks whether Peter will be with us at Nana and Grandad's on Christmas Day. We take immense delight in saying, 'yes, we hope our little boy will definitely be part of the family by the time Christmas comes around'.

Congratulations and a multitude of gifts arrive from all and sundry. Rob's work colleagues astound me with their generosity. I swear we receive far more presents than we would have done if I'd just given birth to a baby!

Peter's foster carer is due to come down to see us next Tuesday, along with Clare. They are going to bring some photos of Peter for us to keep, and at long last we will be able to show everyone what our son looks like. That will be a wonderful feeling.

As Tuesday approaches, Rob and I become more and more excited. We are especially keen to meet Peter's foster carer for, after all, she knows our son better than anyone else. Peter has lived with her family for over a year now, so it will be good to get a real feel for him from someone so close, as well as hearing all about his routines and his favourite things.

Tuesday 12 August 2003

Tim gets here early to see if there is anything we need to discuss before the meeting. He also runs through the list of questions we have prepared for the foster carer. When she arrives, we are delighted to find that she is such a warm, friendly, and easy person to talk to. This is such a relief, as we know that we will have to work closely with her in the future. Not only has she brought a whole stack of photos for us to look at and keep, but she has also brought a video, some of it filmed only the day before. The photos are fabulous – really expressive action shots and so many pictures of Peter laughing. He looks a happy little boy and has the most impish smile ever.

The video is wonderful. It really brings Peter alive for us, as we watch him running around with ducks on a recent holiday and playing with his toys at home. Seeing the video does feel surreal – watching our son-to-be talking into a camera only twenty-four hours before. Robbie and I spend a long time chatting with Peter's foster carer. She couldn't be nicer and we can both really empathise with her. It is going to be tough for her to part with Peter.

It is arranged that a lot of Peter's belongings will be coming with him, like his stroller, car seat and bedding. It will help him to settle in and feel more comfortable, as otherwise, everything at our house will be new to him. Rob and I are asked if we can make a video of ourselves, the dogs, our house and the town where we live. We are also asked to prepare a photo album that will be taken to Peter before he meets us, so that he can become familiar with our pictures.

We talk a lot about preparing for the introductions to Peter – pencilled in for late autumn – a few weeks after his third birthday. For the first week Robbie and I will be staying in Peter's home town, visiting him for an hour at first, then an afternoon, then getting him up first thing in the morning and so on until he trusts us enough to take him out on our own, prepare his tea and put him to bed. Then Rob and I will return home, collect the dogs from the kennels and continue with the introductions at our house. Peter will travel down with his foster carer and they will stay at a nearby hotel. Every meeting will be taken at Peter's pace. Nothing will be rushed or forced, and although the time span is pencilled in for two weeks, a lot of flexibility will be allowed. A review at our house, a week into the introductions, will help everyone to assess how things are going.

After the meeting we have great fun collecting together all the pictures of our family for the album. It feels strange to imagine our three-year-old son turning over the pages, seeing pictures of his new mummy and daddy for the first time. Very scary for him – such a leap into the unknown. It will be a similar leap into the unknown for us, of course, but at least we are adults and can make sense of what is happening. It will seem very confusing to a three-year-old. He will surely need masses of reassurance, love and patience – and so, for that matter, will we.

The next stage of the proceedings for us is to redesign Peter's bedroom in our house and to start buying all those extra bits and pieces such as stair gates, toy boxes, bedding and clothes.

Late August–September 2003

We have the best time ever, buying all and sundry for Peter's bedroom. We are hoping to recreate a look similar to his room in the foster carers' home. We choose bright blue wallpaper, Tweenies bedding, Winnie The Pooh pictures and masses of cuddly toys and books. We have to guess Peter's actual size from the photos, so choosing clothes is a bit of a gamble – and we know that some things will probably swamp him like a tent! It doesn't matter, these are absolutely magical weeks, as all of our hopes and dreams turn into reality.

We constantly email the foster carer (especially around Peter's third birthday, though it is hard not being able to join in the celebrations). This proves invaluable in helping us feel connected to what is happening at the other end of the country. Tim is also brilliant in phoning and keeping us up to date with what is going on.

One thing that is particularly painful to hear, however, is how upset Peter has become at the thought of moving away from the foster carers' home. This is entirely understandable and not unexpected, but it is still really distressing. Rob and I feel powerless to help, which of course we are. It certainly takes the shine off our sense of jubilation, and we just hope that things will start to get easier for Peter as time goes on.

Sure enough, Peter gradually becomes less upset at the prospect of moving although he is still rather bemused by the whole thing. Robbie and I send some recent photos of the dogs and us, as well as some postcards of our town and the nearby seaside. We also send a map, so that Peter will be able to understand where the "South of England" is exactly!

We then begin to put together our video for Peter. We spend many a day filming our dogs playing and we do our very best to try and convey our love and warmth through the lens of a camera. I so want our son to enjoy it. It is harder than we imagine to pick out all the fun things which might be of interest to a small child. Showing Peter his bedroom (with the aid of some hand puppets!) we hope will be a winner. We have spent so much time getting his bedroom right and we hope it will remind Peter of his present room – to make the transition from one home to another just that little bit easier.

As the weeks progress, heading towards our last but all important panel, which will be asked to recommend our match with Peter, we go through another gamut of emotions, everything from fear to euphoria. It is an incredible time, and friends who have adopted say that they felt the same way.

After what seems an age, the weeks and days suddenly accelerate rather too quickly. Before we know it, we are only one week away from panel and introductions, and preparing for our last visit from our social worker, Tim. Neither of us can really believe that in seven days' time we will be meeting our son for the very first time. Words cannot do justice to how we are feeling.

Monday 13 October 2003

The meeting with Tim goes well – he calms our nerves and shares our pleasure. He likes the bedroom and thinks that the album of family pictures is great.

We talk about the final preparations for panel in a couple of days. Neither of us has to attend which, quite frankly, we are rather glad about. Tim will be representing us and he will hand over the video and photo album to Clare, to take to the foster carer's house. Peter will then be able to look at them as many times as he wants, before we eventually arrive the following Tuesday.

Tim also talks us through our impending meeting with Peter's birth mother, which is taking place the day before we get to meet Peter. Both Rob and I have more misgivings and feel more apprehensive about this meeting than we have about anything else so far. Tim will also be present, as well as Clare, who will be supporting Peter's birth mother.

We keep reminding ourselves that we have agreed to this meeting for Peter's sake. We will get the chance to ask certain questions and it could be good for Peter's birth mother, hopefully, to come away from the meeting feeling a little more positive about the two people who will be raising her son. All very difficult, and I have a feeling that our meeting may get somewhat emotional.

I'll never forget these few days before we meet Peter. Our panel date passes without complications, apart from yet another reprimand about my smoking. We are now on the final countdown to what the adoption process has been about. Everything becomes a whirlwind of activity. We frantically buy the last few bits for the house and enjoy some time out for just the two of us. We fill the cupboards with child-friendly foods. Then, before we know it, it is the night before we are due to drive up north to our hotel – which will be our home for the next seven nights.

Sunday 19 October 2003

We are elated and feel physically sick. Morning is here and we are packing our suitcases into the car. It really is happening. We are about to meet our son and the next chapter of our life will begin.

Peter, I hope and pray that you will like your new mummy and daddy, and I promise you that we will do everything in our power to make you feel a safe and happy little boy.

October–December 2003

To our son

I dreamt of you last night, even though I have yet to meet you. I dreamt that I took your hand and held you with my love.

I know it will not be that easy – but this morning, when I woke, I also knew that no matter how hard it may be, your new mummy and daddy will always be there to look after you.

And to love you. Forever.

That is our pledge to you.

Tuesday 21 October 2003

I catch my breath as I glimpse our son standing at the foster carers' front door, a beaming smile etched upon his face, his hand waving madly.

It is 2pm on Tuesday afternoon and we are due to take Peter to the park with his foster carer. It will be a short meeting – a couple of hours; we are supposed to act as naturally as possible, while introducing ourselves as Peter's new mummy and daddy!

That first meeting is heaven – although no, you do not fall in love instantly, as any truthful adopter will tell you. But we do feel a rush of affection towards this child. We also feel slightly awkward, anxious and anything but natural.

We have imagined this moment for years, and suddenly here we are, examining every single inch of our child's face. We struggle to take it all in. Now we are parents. Perhaps this is akin to holding your newborn baby in your arms for that very first time. The moment will stay with me forever, of that I'm sure. It is one of those landmarks in our lives that we will re-live a thousand times over.

Wednesday 22 October 2003

We have a very early start, so that we can arrive before Peter wakes up. This is when we both begin to feel quite alarmingly out of our depth – standing in someone else's house – watching whilst a family (with other foster children) goes about its daily routine. It is 6am, still dark outside, and we are not yet fully awake after an almost sleepless night. To make matters worse, Peter is not in the best of moods when he wakes; he is confused as to why we are there and who we are. We see the first glimpses of an explosive temper.

We have been told about his tantrums, of course, but witnessing little fists flying is another thing entirely. Peter is finding the attention and disruption to his routine unsettling. We have been warned that this might be the case, and on this second day of introductions, the reality begins to hit home.

Thursday 23 October 2003

On the third morning, Robbie and I are expected to prepare Peter's breakfast, which fortunately he loves. Both of us still feel ill at ease in the foster carers' house; we also feel extremely sorry for them, having two strangers descend on them at six in the morning and take over. It feels horribly artificial and contributes to me having problems assessing my true feelings about the whole adoption, coupled with the fact that I have a nasty chest infection and I am seriously sleep-deprived.

Being holed up in a noisy hotel for a week, away from family, friends and anything "familiar" is also hard. Both of us are feeling the strain and sensing an overall lack of support. The meeting we endured on arrival in Peter's home town was nothing short of awful. Every single moment of the two-week introduction was dissected in minute detail. Tensions and emotions were running high and not everyone around the table seemed to agree with all the finer details of the plan. The foster carers kept breaking down in tears and Clare was looking more and more annoyed. At the end of the meeting we were handed a stack of life story books and other documents and then left to make our way back to the hotel. Neither Tim nor Clare nor anyone seemed concerned about how we might be feeling. It was disappointing and the cracks were starting to show.

Thursday afternoon

One thing that does go remarkably well is the meeting with Peter's birth mother. This is pencilled in for this afternoon, and when the moment comes I am within an inch of saying that I can't go through with it. But in the end I do. The meeting is delayed by two hours, so by the time we're taken to the social services department to meet Peter's birth mother, we are making ourselves ill with anxiety. We have been plied with so much discouraging information that it is fair to say that we are not at all keen to meet her.

Clare keeps reassuring us that it will be fine and that she 'knows how to handle Peter's mother'. Tim remains calm throughout. The meeting itself is fairly short and Peter's mother is as nice as could be. My heart goes out to her, and all I want to do is hug her. She seems so alone, and I feel guilty for wanting to become Peter's new mother. She is very young and immature and quiet throughout our exchange. At the end of the meeting we have our photo taken together, to be placed in one of Peter's numerous life story books.

We promise to maintain letterbox contact once a year, with photos included. No matter how much she may have neglected or failed Peter in the past, we feel she deserves this at least. We just hope that she will not get herself pregnant again, as Clare fears. For if she does, the whole sad cycle might be repeated, and she will lose another child.

Friday 24–Sunday 26 October 2003

We gradually begin to enjoy more quality time alone with Peter, taking him out for the afternoon, feeding the ducks, taking photos, playing, having a hug and walking together. These moments are lovely. Initially Peter has bonded with Robbie more quickly than with me, which hurts, so when he begins to call me "Mummy" and doesn't always turn to the foster carer instead of me, it is truly wonderful. Clearly, Peter is still finding introductions rather confusing, and is prone to some fairly knee-jerk tantrums. He will call me "mummy" when out, then call the foster carer "mum" when we return. It must be painfully hard for this little boy to even begin to know to whom to turn. My own emotions are certainly being pushed to their limits this week. And so are the foster carer's. This lady has the unenviable task of having to distance herself from a child who has been in her care for over a year. She tries to remain supportive and encouraging to us both, as do her husband and younger son.

Although we have a couple of successful outings to nature reserves and parks, as well as an award-winning tantrum in McDonalds, when Peter flings himself on the floor like a starfish, both Robbie and I are keen to be back on our own home turf. We really need to start feeling like a proper family and in control of the situation. Peter also seems eager to meet our two dogs; the foster carers have dogs, so it is something he is comfortable with. We are keen to collect them from the kennels and see how that first meeting will go.

Before we return down south, Clare and some fellow social workers join us at the foster family's house for a "pause and reflect" meeting. We tell Tim not to worry about making the three hour-long-journey; with hindsight, it would have been infinitely better if he had been present. The meeting is excruciating – everyone firing questions at us, our emotions ragged by this point. I begin to feel threatened, and even start to doubt my own abilities to be a parent.

After much deliberation, it is decided to see how the introductions continue on our home territory. Our departure proves to be very traumatic for Peter, mainly because he sees us packing a lot of his toys and clothes into our jeep. This will be Peter's sixth move in three years and he becomes hysterical at the prospect, lashing out at the foster carer and screaming in sheer confusion. It is both heartbreaking and frightening to witness.

When we eventually arrive back home, it is fantastic to be on familiar ground again. I can't help feeling that perhaps we should have done this earlier. We indicate to Tim and Clare that it would be good to have more time alone with Peter as we feel he needs to be given the clear message that Robbie and I are his new "permanent" mummy and daddy. They agree wholeheartedly – and so does the foster carer. Tea for everyone on Day 1 is reduced to tea for Peter, Robbie and myself.

Tuesday 28 October 2003

Peter does not seem unduly concerned by the foster carers leaving after they drop him at our house; he probably realises that he will see them later on. We have a good time together and Peter instantly bonds with our two dogs, who become his newest playmates. He loves his bedroom and even asks if he may stay the night with us, snuggled under his Tweenies duvet. We have to say 'no, not tonight' as he is not yet allowed to stay over. We make the most of the time available, playing with bubbles and playdoh and crayoning crazy pictures. Gleeful shouts of 'Mummy' as we prepare tea together simply make my heart melt.

Wednesday 29–Friday 31 October 2003

We collect Peter every morning from the foster carers' rented cottage. Normally this produces a massive (and very distressing) tantrum, as he doesn't want to leave the foster carers' son. We sometimes have to physically restrain Peter in order to get him into the car seat; by the time we get back to our house, he has normally quietened down.

In general Peter's moods are very up and down – as you would expect from a muddled and insecure three-year-old. One minute he is playing games, squealing with delight, and the next he is screaming in our faces and kicking at the dogs. We are very aware that most of this behaviour is due to his circumstances. Some of it is simply down to the fact that Peter is a normal, boisterous and very strong-willed three-year-old boy!

In the middle of this second week, we have another review to see how things are going. Clare and Tim come to our house and watch us playing together. Peter is in a good mood and eats his lunch beautifully at the table. We all play with his bubble gun and do masses of jigsaws. Both social workers seem pleased, and Rob and I are feeling much happier and more confident. It is decided that Peter will move in with us for good in two days' time. The foster carers will come in for a quick cup of tea, some last minute photos, and then they will leave for their return journey home.

It has also been decided that we will not go back north to say our goodbyes; it had seemed a bad idea to us in the first place to drag Peter back to the foster carers' house, just to say goodbye. It is too long a journey to go there and back in one day – and everyone is of the opinion that Peter will become even more confused if he goes back to his previous home, only to be wrenched away again. He is already upset each time we pick him up from the holiday cottage. So, on the last two days of introductions the foster carers will drop Peter off at our house instead. This seems to work a whole lot better. Things really start to improve on our last two outings with Peter, although Clare feels that an overnight stay would not be a good idea. She thinks we should wait until he moves in with us for good. We now feel prepared for that moment, even though we still have to pinch ourselves to believe that it's really happening.

Saturday 1 November 2003

I cannot convey how Rob and I feel when we wake in the morning and realise that our son moves in with us today. It will be our last "lie-in" (until 7am – Peter normally wakes at about five!). It will be our last few moments together as a couple. It will be my last morning yearning to be a mum. We will finally be a family, we will finally have our son.

Robbie and I are awed by the immensity of what we are taking on. The foster carers have been extremely supportive over the last few days, but everyone's emotions are just about wrung dry. There have been times when I've wanted to crawl under the duvet and fast forward six months, just to see how we have settled down. The constant pressure on us as a couple is relentless and unforgiving. We are lucky in that we have such a strong relationship to support one another, Robbie is especially caring as my health is beginning to suffer. In the first week of introductions I lost three-quarters of a stone in weight. It has undoubtedly been a testing two weeks.

In our workshops, some eighteen months ago now, we were warned that introductions would be physically and emotionally exhausting. We were also told that any seemingly dormant feelings regarding infertility might rear their ugly head again – and yes, they did. But neither Robbie nor I feel that we were prepared enough for the strain of a long distance adoption, especially that of a three-year-old, whose capacity to understand what was going on must have been next to nothing. If *I* can hardly describe how tough the last two weeks have been, then for a vulnerable little boy it must have been hell.

The morning passes in a blur. The foster carers arrive at nine, stay for tea and photos and leave quietly and without any fuss, their emotions bravely concealed from Peter. Peter is fairly nonchalant about their leaving, but then we knew he would be, as he couldn't possibly comprehend that they are going back to their home without him. The day goes well; it is somewhat strange perhaps, but immense fun when we visit a nearby nature centre. Rob and I try hard to pick up on Peter's feelings. He likes his dinner, as well as his bath; his bedtime story is followed by a surprisingly easy drift off to sleep.

As Rob and I enjoy a celebratory glass of wine downstairs, we are like rabbits caught in headlamps – the television barely audible and talking in no more than a whisper. It is quite comical really, especially when we venture to bed, hardly daring to breathe in case we wake our gorgeous new son.

Reproduced from *An Adoption Diary*, by Maria James, published by BAAF in 2006 (pp 72–89). © Maria James

Two dads = two people to play football with!

Thursday 18th March

As the date for introductions approaches – less than three weeks now – one big milestone is that Charlie has to be told he is moving on from his foster home to a new family. We talked to Annie, his foster carer, about this. Charlie has been in a home where he feels happy and safe. Why would he want to move? Annie assured us that Charlie has always known his current home is temporary, and as much as he likes it, he's really looking forward to moving on to his new family. He has been in that foster home for nearly three years, and he's seen other children move on to live with their new families. Apparently, when people visit the house, he tells them that he's hoping to be adopted soon.

In a recent conversation in the foster home, Annie explained to the children that a family could be a mum and a dad, or just one mum or one dad, two mums or two dads. Annie told us that Charlie was intrigued by all these possibilities. A little girl who was in the same foster home went to a new family with two mums and apparently he liked the idea, so the foster carer has been doing some work about adoption by same-sex couples using some relevant pages from the book *Dad David, Baba Chris and Me*, which tells the story of a boy who is adopted by a male mixed ethnicity couple. She also told us that the other day he said that he didn't think he liked the idea of having two dads, but when she told him that two dads meant two people to play football with, instead of one, he changed his mind! I guess this is something that she will work on more as she prepares to tell him about us and to show him our introductions book. That won't be until a few days before we meet him, so that his excitement and expectations can be managed.

Friday 19th March

It's St. Joseph's day, which in Spain is Father's Day, so it couldn't have been better timing when we got the call from Miranda this afternoon to tell us that the decision maker at the placing authority has confirmed the panel's recommendation for the match with Charlie. It's now official! Although we'd been told that it was almost certain that this would be the case, it was fantastic to have the confirmation. We should get a letter tomorrow or Monday, and shortly after we should get the official bit of paper that will allow us to apply for paternity and adoption leave from our employers. It's really happening!

* * *

Monday 29th March

We're one week away from meeting our son! Today was my last day at work. It feels weird to think that I don't have a number of jobs waiting to be done, but it was great to write 'I won't be back until next year' on my out of office email auto-reply!

Today there was a bit of a panic as Charlie's social worker is on holiday and nobody knew whether our introductions book and DVD had arrived. On Wednesday she will tell him that he's being placed with a family and then show him our book and DVD, so they need to be there.

After a few hours of confusion, someone located them, so that was OK. We've also sent him a short story I wrote and illustrated about our road to adoption, and how we hope to make good dads for him; it also deals with the fact that he's going to have two dads and not a mum and dad. I wasn't really sure whether it was appropriate or not, but we showed it to Miranda last week and she liked it, so it went in the post this morning.

We've been in touch with the foster carer trying to sort out what to bring for introductions. She has suggested that as well as the cuddly penguin we've already agreed on, we should bring a Lego toy. That way, on the second or third day, we can sit down and build it together, which will give Charlie a chance to play with us but keep his distance if he needs to (as not a lot of eye contact is necessary). Apparently he's very good with Lego, so we'll be able to praise him on how well he does.

* * *

Friday 2nd April

Sarah, Charlie's social worker, went to visit him on Wednesday. She sent us an email to let us know how it went. We also spoke to Annie, his foster carer, who gave us her account. Sarah told Charlie she had news for him and could he guess what it might be. Charlie said 'No', but he clung to Annie and she could tell that he knew what was coming. Sarah told him they'd found new parents for him and he cried a little. Both Annie and Sarah think that this is a great sign as he's not bottling up his feelings, but it's still hard for us to hear. He was bound to feel a lot of mixed emotions about finally moving on to a new family and leaving Annie's home.

Sarah told him he would have two dads and showed him our book and puzzle. Apparently he was delighted with them. He liked the pictures of his room and the fact that Daddy Mike is a Beaver leader and he'll be able to join his group. He also liked the garden and he noticed all the pictures of him that we've placed all over the house. He was very impressed with that. He spotted Tango the penguin too. As soon as he'd seen the whole book he ran to Annie's husband to tell him all about it and share his news. He seemed really positive about having two dads, and that evening when he went to a school disco (I know, a school disco at six?) he told his best friend about it. They didn't show him the DVD at that point, but they did show him the story I wrote for him and apparently he loved it. In fact Annie told us she cried when she read it to him!

When he went to bed he took his book with him. Both Sarah and Annie agree that it's gone as they hoped it would. He's nervous about meeting us next week, but Annie pointed out to him that we are nervous about meeting him too.

Annie also told us that the DVD we sent is among the best she's ever seen – although she probably says that to every adoptive parent – and she laughed at the collection of out-takes we included. Both Mike and I were welling up when we heard from Annie and Sarah. It's such a relief to know that Charlie's fine about having two dads and looking forward to meeting us. We may ring Annie again on Sunday to find out how he does once the news sinks in.

* * *

Monday 5th April

We're back from Spain now. We've received a letter from our local education authority confirming a place for Charlie in our chosen school, which is fantastic.

Miranda rang, even though it's a bank holiday! Charlie's family finder spoke to his birth parents. They had some questions and the family finder was able to answer them, so they feel reassured and even willing to meet us! Miranda thinks that part of the problem was that Sarah simply wrote them a letter to inform them that a gay couple was adopting Charlie instead of actually visiting them and explaining everything. We will meet them separately for thirty minutes each towards the end of introductions. We're not looking forward to it, as it won't be comfortable, but we really welcome the opportunity to ask them about Charlie, and to hear anything they can tell us about him.

Miranda also told us that our attachment-focused counselling will have to start after the placement now, as Charlie's local authority haven't arranged it yet. This is a pity, as we were meant to do a couple of sessions before meeting him.

In the evening we rang Annie to see how Charlie's been doing since he was told about us last Wednesday. A little boy picked up the phone and I was really thrown as I feared it might be Charlie. After a few seconds I managed to ask if Annie was in and she came to the phone laughing. She'd asked her grandson, who is staying with her, to answer the phone, and then remembered she'd asked us to ring, so she figured I must have thought it was Charlie. After that she told me that Charlie's last day at school on Thursday had been really emotional. He took the introductions book with him and showed it to his classmates at the end of the day. A lot of them cried and their mums and teacher cried too! He also had a long hug with his best mate and told him it was OK to be sad because it was a sad moment! Charlie cried quite a bit, but Annie was really pleased about this as only six months ago he'd have said he didn't care and he hated everyone anyway, so it showed how capable of attachment and expressing his feelings he's become.

One of his classmates asked him why he was moving to another family. Annie heard him reply that he couldn't live with his mummy and that's why he needed two daddies. Another boy apparently chipped in that having two dads was "gross". One can't help wondering if he heard that from his parents – clearly a six-year-old does not form such opinions, he repeats what he's heard at home. Charlie replied that it wasn't gross, and that he wanted two dads! On the one hand, I feel sad that he's had to experience such an encounter already, on the other, I'm incredibly proud of him for that response!

He's also been watching the DVD we made for him over and over and playing with the puzzle we sent him. When it's finished and our picture is complete he says to everyone 'these are my dads'. Annie told me he's now dropped our names and refers to us as Daddy and Dad. Apparently he's really at ease with the idea of two dads. He's been asking questions about his new school. She also mentioned that he's been tearful and clingy, because although he's excited about moving on to his new family, he's sad to go. I told Annie how happy we were that they are Charlie's foster carers, since they've obviously done such a good job (they've actually won an award for their many years of outstanding foster care), and she said that she thought we were the best match for Charlie and she feels sure that Charlie will want to be with us. He has even said he wants to learn Spanish! He's learned to say "hola" and also, for some reason, how to say "lavadora" (washing machine). Does this mean he'll want to do the washing?

The updates from the foster carer have helped us to push aside the "what if he hates us?" anxiety we've been having as the date for introductions approaches. We're so excited. We're nervous about meeting him but really looking forward to it. Despite our nerves we will do our best to be ourselves. We know the first meeting is likely to be somewhat awkward and that's why we're "only" staying for two hours. Once we have got over the nerves and excitement of tomorrow we can start to get to know each other and do things together in a much more natural way. I don't know how much sleep we'll get tonight. Tomorrow we will meet our son for the first time and all our lives will definitely change forever. We just want everything to go well.

Tuesday 6th April

This morning we got up early and drove to the town where Charlie currently lives. We had a meeting with Sarah and she gave us a whole load of paperwork, including the care order, placement order, and a letter that allows us to authorise minor medical treatment for Charlie. Then we followed her to the foster carers' home. I was uncharacteristically calm and Mike was very nervous. As we pulled up we saw Charlie waving at us behind the glass front door, which took us by surprise. We waved back, parked the car, and went to the door with Sarah. He opened it for us and Sarah introduced us as Daddy Mike and Dad Pablo. We both said how nice it was to finally meet him and he was quite shy, almost hiding behind Annie's legs. He looked just like in the pictures, which I realise is a silly thing to say. We finally met Peter, Annie's husband. Both of them laugh all the time and their home is very welcoming. We went to the living room, where Charlie had started the puzzle with our picture. He finished it fairly quickly, which gave us an opportunity to praise him on how well and how quickly he'd done it. Then we played with a *Ben 10* 3D puzzle that was actually quite difficult. This allowed us to help him and genuinely work together to complete it. Annie mentioned that he's left-handed and I said I am left-handed too. It may seem silly but that really made me feel connected to him, something that we share, almost like it's something that I might have passed on to him if he were my birth son. Charlie seemed pleased to hear I was left-handed too, as if he was thinking the same thing.

Annie took a couple of pictures for his life story book, and with the excuse of posing for the pictures asked him to give each of us a hug. It felt a bit forced, but it was our first hug! After that we helped him put together some paper planes. Annie praised him for his patience and not getting frustrated with the 3D puzzle and the planes, and mentioned how he used to get grumpy. He withdrew a little at that point, but I suggested that he show us his room and he quickly stood up and led us to it. He proudly showed us many of his toys, and Annie helped him to show us the chart Sarah's done for him with the introductions plan for the next two weeks. I asked him if he was ticklish and tickled his foot. His feet aren't ticklish at all! I said that I was and he felt comfortable enough to tickle my feet. The two hours flew by and soon we were saying goodbye. We could tell he was getting a bit stressed by this time, so it was perfect timing. He gave us each a big hug and we left.

We are really pleased with how it went. We weren't sure how we would feel, and it was strange to meet him after everything we've read and heard. We didn't feel a "wave of love" come surging as soon as we saw him. And he didn't come rushing towards us when we first met. We think both of these are good signs. We were nervous and so was he. And we simply do not know each other. We want to love him, and we will. It will come soon enough. We already feel like he's part of our lives. We can't wait to spend a lot more time with him and for our love for him, and his love for us, to grow.

Miranda rang us in the evening to ask how it went and to ask if we want to proceed. We said yes, of course, and she was very pleased. Tomorrow will be a much more "real" experience. We will have got over the nerves of the first meeting and it will feel more natural.

Reproduced from *Becoming Dads*, by Pablo Fernández, published by BAAF in 2011 (pp 126–136).
© Pablo Fernández

Love at first sight?

The first day I met Alan I was sort of in shock, really, and feeling naturally terribly nervous. I knew a lot about Alan and I'd seen some pictures of him. He'd heard of me too. I'd made him a little book about myself, my family and my home, and I knew that his foster mother, whom Alan called Nanny, had been going through the book with him. In the book I'd written 'Hello, my name is Julia,' but Nanny, who knew better, had apparently been saying to him 'Look, Alan, that's Mummy'. Now, Alan had never really called anyone else Mummy. He'd had regular contact with his birth mother, but she didn't figure much in his life. He knew other children had mummies, because his friends at nursery school had mummies who came to collect them at the end of each session. How was he to know what mummies were and how was he to know they didn't just turn up one day out of the blue and claim their little boys, just as I was about to?

When I arrived at the foster family's home, I trembled as I knocked on the door. Nanny opened it, we said hello and then suddenly there was little Alan, bright as a button and very excited. 'Who's this?' Nanny asked. 'It's Mummy,' cried Alan.

* * *

So, at our very first meeting, Alan came running to the door of Nanny's house and recognised me from the pictures he'd seen. I was astonished at this bright little chap who knew I was his mummy. When I remember that moment, in my head it's like one of those romantic wedding pictures that you see, where the couple are in the centre of the picture and they're framed by a sort of blurry line that suggests the mists of time or whatever. The truth is that he came running to the door, with a bottle of sugary drink dripping all over him. He had something horrible and sticky all round his mouth and his nappy, a frankly rather stinky one, was hanging off him. Somehow, although it must have registered somewhere in my memory, I didn't notice that at the time. Love at first sight? Yes, I think so.

Reproduced from *Flying Solo*, by Julia Wise, published by BAAF in 2007 (pp 47–48 and p 55). © Julia Wise

What I would like to find out about the child

....
....
....
....
....
....
....
....
....
....
....
....

What might the differences be?

....
....
....
....
....
....
....
....
....
....
....
....
....
....

MODULE 8: **Telling, contact and social networking**

Learning outcomes

This module aims to help you to:

- **understand the lifelong nature of adoption, for everyone involved**
- **appreciate the importance of birth families in the lives of adopted children**
- **understand why and how you need to talk about adoption with your child**
- **consider the implications of social networking for adoptive families**

Life cycle tasks for adopters

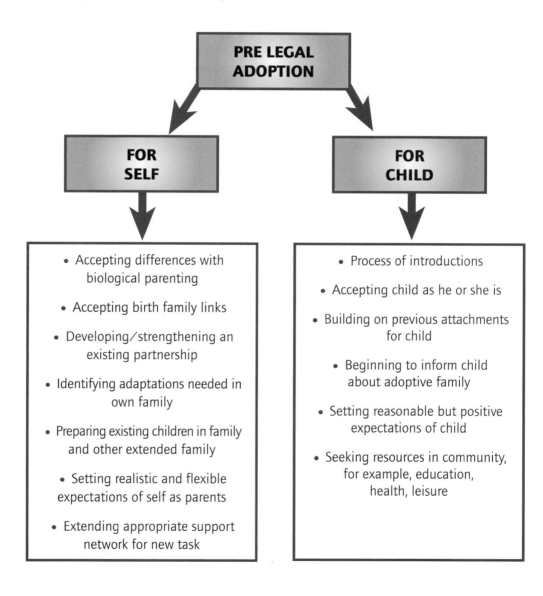

PRE LEGAL ADOPTION

FOR SELF

- Accepting differences with biological parenting
- Accepting birth family links
- Developing/strengthening an existing partnership
- Identifying adaptations needed in own family
- Preparing existing children in family and other extended family
- Setting realistic and flexible expectations of self as parents
- Extending appropriate support network for new task

FOR CHILD

- Process of introductions
- Accepting child as he or she is
- Building on previous attachments for child
- Beginning to inform child about adoptive family
- Setting reasonable but positive expectations of child
- Seeking resources in community, for example, education, health, leisure

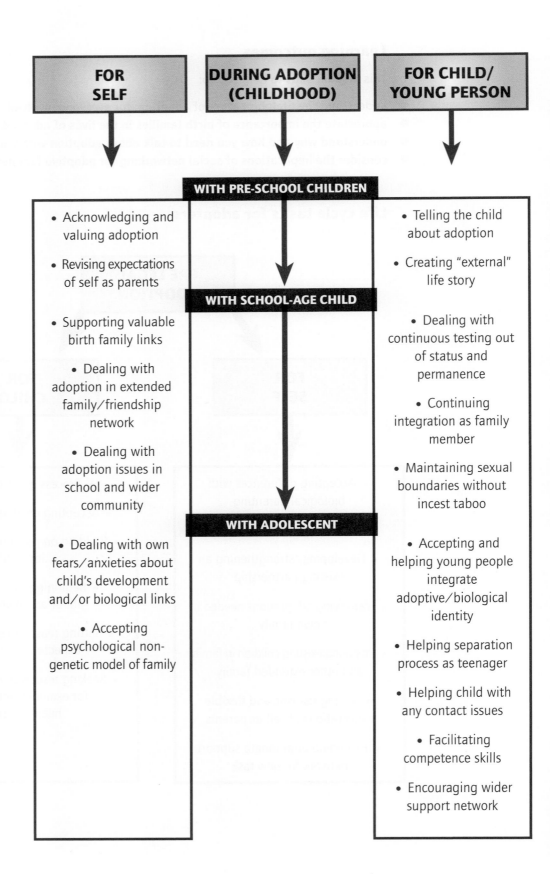

FOR SELF	DURING ADOPTION (CHILDHOOD)	FOR CHILD/ YOUNG PERSON

WITH PRE-SCHOOL CHILDREN

WITH SCHOOL-AGE CHILD

WITH ADOLESCENT

- Acknowledging and valuing adoption

- Revising expectations of self as parents

- Supporting valuable birth family links

- Dealing with adoption in extended family/friendship network

- Dealing with adoption issues in school and wider community

- Dealing with own fears/anxieties about child's development and/or biological links

- Accepting psychological non-genetic model of family

- Telling the child about adoption

- Creating "external" life story

- Dealing with continuous testing out of status and permanence

- Continuing integration as family member

- Maintaining sexual boundaries without incest taboo

- Accepting and helping young people integrate adoptive/biological identity

- Helping separation process as teenager

- Helping child with any contact issues

- Facilitating competence skills

- Encouraging wider support network

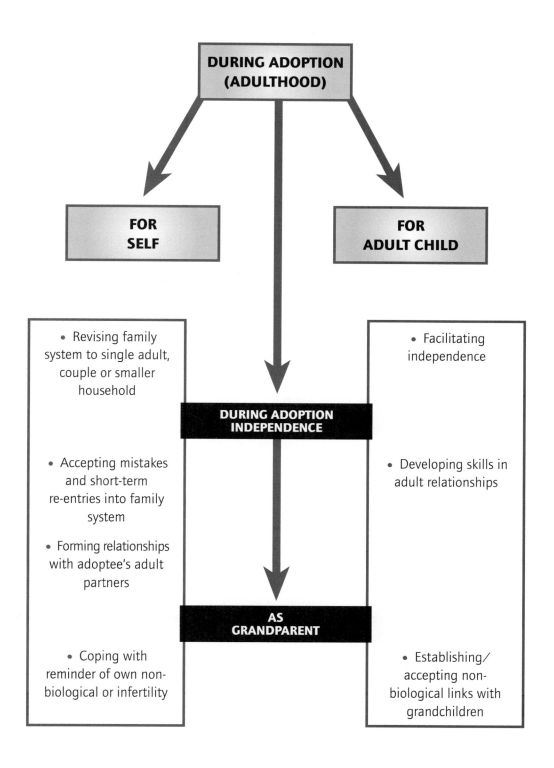

Opening the door

I usually chose the time when she was wrapped in her towel and lying on the mat after her bath – a nice secure time. Obviously it wasn't every bath time but as she learned to talk she would ask me at this particular time to tell her about my visits to the foster home to see her and 'What did we all say?' She, like many children, likes repetition – it seems to give security – and at first it was like another fairy tale for her. Now it's a reality, and a pleasant one.

Although far fewer babies are placed for adoption nowadays, there are thousands and thousands of adopted children and adults in the UK. Families in general vary considerably, with many children experiencing the separation or divorce of parents, forming new relationships with step-parents or spending at least part of their childhood with a single parent. We know all these areas are discussed much more openly now than in the past, including directly with the children concerned. Adoption is also talked about more openly now, both within families and in the wider community, including the media. This, however, does not automatically make it easier for adoptive parents to feel comfortable in approaching discussion of something which is so close to the heart of their family life.

The first step

Adoptive parents often worry about "getting it right". As adults, we may be very aware of all the complex information we have and the amount we may need to share. This first step, however, is about establishing basic communication about adoption and letting your child know it is something that can be talked about. This applies whether your child joined you soon after birth and is relying on you to introduce the subject, or came at a later stage, having done some life story work but needing to find out how you, as his or her new adoptive parents, will respond.

The first step is about opening the door to an important area of your child's life. Children vary tremendously in how they explore things. Some may plunge in with lots of questions for a while, then move on to something else. Others are more cautious and may only want to know very little, before returning to more familiar preoccupations. Many children do not share their concerns through words, either because of their age or because saying some things is too scary. Some children may be aware, or sense, dark corners that will need to be explored slowly and tentatively with your support. Ultimately, a realistic idea of what is there is healthier than undefined fears or fantasies. Older children may be able to gain confidence through being able to share their memories with you and knowing you will listen carefully. They may also wish to keep certain doors closed for a period.

For adults, it can help to think about or rehearse a few simple words to get started – try saying the words in your head to see what comes easily and if there are bits you stumble over. It may help to identify a useful "trigger" event, when the topic could be introduced naturally – perhaps a visit to a former foster home or a celebration of the granting of the adoption order. You may need to consciously create an opening or prompt an older child who can equally feel awkward or uncomfortable about bringing the subject up, and be less equipped to find the right words. Early thinking and planning will help you feel more in control. If you are adopting as partners, one person may feel more confident in taking the lead.

If you convey a positive sense of adoption to your child and he or she grows up knowing that you are willing to talk about their reality, that firm base will stand them in good stead as years go by.

Whatever your child's age, warmth and affection are very important ingredients in sharing information. Body language matters at least as much as the actual words used. Some people show their feelings more readily than others and, equally, your child will be picking up the emotional climate in your family. What matters is that the child does not feel overwhelmed by feelings she or he does not understand or becomes reluctant to bring the topic up again. One of the initial things that you will be picking up from your child is his or her level of comfort with physical affection and how best to offer reassurance. It also helps to have established some family routines that you can use to confirm the security of their place with you.

Reproduced from *Talking about Adoption to your Adopted Child*, by Marjorie Morrison (4th edition), published by BAAF in 2012 (pp 13–15). © BAAF

Telling your child the adoption story

The importance of being open

Adopted children will benefit from being raised in a family where adoption is discussed from a young age and in an open and understandable way. Keeping secrets about the past can damage their identity formation; it can also damage their trust in you. If your child does not know the facts from an early age, she may, during primary school, make up wild fantasies about her birth parents or about the reasons why she was given up for adoption. She may also develop split feelings of loyalty between you and her birth parents. If adoptive parents don't, or very seldom, talk about the adoption, children might not know for sure whether they are allowed to ask or fantasise about their birth parents; they may think that it isn't fair to their adoptive parents. They may also start feeling scared that they may be abandoned or rejected again. During puberty, and later on in life, this insecurity can lead to an even greater confusion. By covering up the truth, you may be creating a vacuum where all the fantasies, thoughts and feelings collide together more and more furiously.

Holding back essential information creates "family secrets" that most probably will be unravelled some day, with all the unwelcome consequences. For instance, your young child may accidentally hear some of the facts from other people, and this could lead to inner withdrawal or to outwardly aggressive behaviour. If your child discovers the truth at an older age from documents, from someone else or (eventually) from you, she will have to rebuild her identity and her trust in you will inevitably be damaged.

If you want to build a strong bond with your child, you should be honest about her adoption history from the very moment she comes to live with you. This naturally doesn't mean that you tell a two-year-old the same story as you would tell a six- or eight-year-old. Toddlers have a very different reality to slightly older children or to children in primary school. They will therefore also have a different understanding of their adoption.

The importance of gathering information

Showing an interest in being open begins before and during the actual adoption. From the moment you receive the first details about your child, it is important that you collect as much information as possible about her medical and social history. Of course, there may be very little information available but try, in any case, to gather as much as you can.

- Before you travel to collect your child, make a list of questions you will want to ask the authorities, the staff in the institutions, the carers or the (foster) parents. What do you want to know about your child's birth, relinquishment, history, care, the environment, the family, etc?
- Remember that your child has the right to know as much as possible, so don't be put off by institutions that prefer not to share information with you. Don't be embarassed to offer a gift or money in order to visit the orphanage. Sometimes a doctor may be willing to provide information but was simply not asked to do so.
- Look around, photograph the environment, and try to speak to people who may know something about your child's past. Write down their names and addresses, and if they are related to your child, write down anything relating to their birth, their education, their health, their occupation, and so on (preferably with relevant dates).
- If your child was a foundling, try to track down any information that was circulated at the time your child was taken into care in an attempt to find the birth parents or other family members.
- When at home, you can continue searching for information through the internet or by contacting email groups of parents who have also adopted a child from the same region. You could possibly make contact with local authorities abroad and set up a donation project in order to stay in touch with the people in the birthplace of your child. It is precisely during these first years that information relating to your child and her birth family may be uncovered. These details will be very important to your child at a later stage.

What do I tell my child and at what age?

Many parents think that their toddlers and very young children will not be able to comprehend their adoption history, so parents put off the difficult moment of telling their child "the truth". However, parents often underestimate their child's level of understanding. According to Bruner (quoted in Kohnstamm, 2002, pp. 106–107), you can, in principle, make everything understandable to a child if the information is adapted to their specific level of understanding.

Bruner is also convinced that new vocabulary can lead to a new way of thinking. The more varied the language that is available to your child, the clearer her thoughts will be. You can give your child a head start by talking freely about her adoption history from a very young age. In this way, your child will learn additional vocabulary and can learn about the relationship between the words and the reality. If she understands these relationships, then she can also have new thoughts about adoption. By doing this, your young child can register the truth and digest it before emotionally coming to terms with the adoption at a later stage. She will not suddenly have to be confronted with totally new information, because she already knows the facts, but from about age seven or eight, she will be able to focus on what she really feels. If there is openness and trust between you, she will not be troubled by questions like 'Is there any information that I am not aware of?', and 'Can I believe you?'

An additional reason to start talking to your child about her adoption at an early age is that it gives you the chance to practise telling a difficult story. Talking about it to a young child is easier because the facts have been simplified. You can slowly add a little more information without your child suddenly experiencing it as difficult or painful.

Another positive reason for starting this conversation at this stage is that it gives your child the signal that adoption is a valued subject and that she can talk about it whenever she wants to. The openness that you achieve by talking about the adoption at the beginning can be maintained and increased if you regularly talk about adoption to your child.

Reproduced from *Adoption Conversations*, by Renée Wolfs, published by BAAF in 2008 (pp 42–45). © Renée Wolfs

THE IMPORTANCE OF BIRTH RELATIVES

The role of contact

Be clear about the purpose of contact

Imagine what it would be like if you woke up one morning and realised that you would never see any of your family or friends again? Or if you found yourself in a strange bed in a strange house surrounded by people who clearly expected you to love them and become an important part of their lives. Where would your heart and mind be in this situation? How much could you focus on being with these new people while all the time you were wondering what had become of your own family and friends and how you would ever recover from the heartbreak of never seeing them again? It is important to keep this type of scenario in mind when we make decisions about the role of contact in the lives of adopted and permanently fostered children.

Current legislation in the UK favours the concept that children placed in permanent families can benefit from knowledge about, and possibly meetings with, members of their birth family. The notion that children need a "clean break" with their past has been replaced with an awareness that "openness" towards the concept of children being part of two families is beneficial to children's welfare, development and sense of identity.

This is reflected in UK legislation, which states that contact may continue to be beneficial for a child even if they will not be returning to their birth family, as long as the child's welfare is paramount, as such contact can keep alive a sense of the child's origins, and may help to keep open options for family relationships in the child's adult life.

However, this is not an encouragement to assume that every child will benefit from contact in every set of circumstances. Agencies which create a blanket policy that presupposes that all older children will benefit from contact are as likely to get it wrong as are agencies which assume that contact for babies is unnecessary. Ensuring that contact is always kept high on the agenda for consideration does not mean that contact will automatically happen; it simply ensures that all the options have been carefully addressed for each individual child.

Ask yourself who contact is for

Contact is for the child or young person. It may help the birth family to cope with separation and it may enable the adopters to understand more about their child's heritage and previous life, but if the child's needs are not paramount, contact will fail to serve its purpose. Contact should only take place when there are clearly identified benefits for the individual child – never as a sop to ease the pain of the birth family.

When considering how contact may benefit the child, you need to ask the following questions:

- Will contact prevent the child from being torn between dividing loyalties, and enable the child to accept a new family more readily?
- Will contact help the child to settle into their new family by reassuring them that family members are OK and still care about them?
- Will contact help the child to understand why they are unable to live with their birth family?
- Will contact promote the child's development by giving them a sense of identity and an understanding of how they fit into the world?
- Will contact enable the child to continue relationships that have been positive and beneficial to them in the past?
- Will contact enable the child to develop relationships which will become more important to them as they grow older?
- Will contact help the child to come to terms with past events?
- Will contact re-traumatise a child by bringing them into proximity with someone who abused them or failed to protect them from harm in the past, and make the child question their new family's ability to protect them?
- Will contact reassure a child of their adopters'/long-term foster carers' ability to protect them from harm, while enabling them to salvage positive aspects of former relationships?
- Will contact enable a child to develop an understanding of how people can hold many different types of relationships in their lives, knowing that some people are part of the everyday world and some are seen less frequently and perhaps only on specific occasions?

It is important to remember that these questions can't be answered once and for all. Children's needs change and family circumstances alter over time, and reviews of contact arrangements will be needed as the child grows older.

Contact is a minefield of emotion and, in our 12 years' experience, changes and shifts all the time. What you have to remember is that you are not doing it for yourselves or for the birth family, but for your children – for their future, for their needs, and to make their passage to adulthood easier.

(Jo, adoptive mother, quoted in *Contact in Adoption and Permanent Foster Care* (Neil and Howe, 2005))

How often and with what aim?

When considering issues around how often an individual child should have contact, it is important to be very clear about its aim. If the aim is for a child to maintain or build on a relationship, then the contact must be frequent enough for it to be meaningful for the child. This will be particularly true of younger children for whom a year seems a very long period, during which people can easily be forgotten. So, even if regular visits are not possible, then frequent telephone contact or letters can help to keep the person present in the child's mind.

However, if the purpose of contact is to create a sense of identity for the child, then less frequent meetings or exchanges of information may be more appropriate. It should still not be forgotten that a very young child is likely to need more regular contact than an older child, to "embed" people into their consciousness.

When thinking about the frequency and purpose of any type of contact, you should consider whether the child needs to sustain or develop a relationship, or to develop an awareness of their connections with these people. A card which says 'Happy birthday, with love from your sister, Beth' can mean the world to a child who has regular contact with their sister. For a child who has little or no contact, such an exchange will merely raise questions about how their sibling is (or indeed, who their sibling is!) and how other family members are doing. Without sufficient accompanying information about their sibling, the child may receive few, if any, benefits from this type of exchange.

Will everyone be clear about the purpose of contact and will this affect the way they respond to contact? Does any support need to be offered to help adopters, foster carers or birth families understand this?

Recognise that contact can help children settle into new placements

There used to be a widely held assumption that contact during the early stages of a placement would be very disruptive for the child. Instead, the opposite may be true. A child who has bonded closely to their foster family may experience a powerful feeling of loss which will interfere with their ability to settle in their adoptive family. A child who is torn between their love for and loyalty towards their birth family and their desire to become a member of their new family may become preoccupied with their feelings of separation and their anxieties about what is happening to their birth family. Contact with members of their foster family and birth family can be very important during these early stages, and can reassure the child that these people are still well and present in their lives and continue to care about them.

It is usual to bring the existing foster carers and new adopters together to plan for the child's move into the family; this should include details about the type and frequency of contact the child will have with their previous foster carers. In the early stages it may be important for the child to see the carers fairly regularly, for example, once a week, and also to receive regular phone calls and cards. As the child settles into the new family, the frequency of this contact with the foster family will decrease, although some form of ongoing contact will still be important.

Adopters – who may connect the concept of contact with birth families – may need help to understand why this contact with foster families is so important in helping the child to settle. Similarly, seeing or speaking to members of the birth family and foster family during the early stages of a new placement can be very reassuring for the child. The child can realise that the birth family has not somehow been obliterated from their lives forever, and that their birth relatives do not think they have vanished or come to serious harm, so does not need to worry about this. Even if the meetings or phone conversations are tinged with pain or sadness, the child can recognise that they are not being expected to shut off all memories of their previous lives and of the people who matter a great deal to them.

Even if more "direct" contact is not possible between the child and birth relatives, it can still be enormously reassuring for the child to know that their birth family is receiving information about them through letters or messages from other relatives.

Foster carers and birth relatives who can clearly show the child that, although they miss them and value them, they wish them well in their permanent family and feel this is a good place for them to be, can play a powerful role in giving "permission" for the child to settle in their new placement.

Don't overlook relationships with other children and young people

Children's relationships with the children of their foster carers and other foster children living with the foster family may also have played a very pivotal role in their lives. A child may have developed a close friendship with another foster child or begun to regard their carer's children as their brothers and sisters. Severing these links can be just as painful as losing contact with birth family members. These important relationships should never be overlooked in making arrangements for contact.

Contact can help children develop a sense of heritage and ethnic identity

Well planned contact has the potential to help all permanently placed children to develop a sense of their identity as they grow up. However, for children who are transracially placed, contact with relatives and/or information about their heritage, culture, religion and customs can be particularly important.

Contact with relatives who live overseas may be potentially difficult to arrange or sustain, but it can be extremely beneficial for children who may otherwise grow up with many questions about their heritage and family circumstances, and the reason they were placed for adoption. The use of email (with appropriate confidentiality built in, where required) can be a good way for children and their adopters to stay in contact with birth families living overseas.

Contact for disabled children

The emotional and identity needs of children and young people with severe learning or communication disabilities may be overlooked if adults assume that contact will confuse or be meaningless for the child. It is probably quite understandable that people might seek to protect a child who they feel is already having to cope with so many difficulties and disadvantages. However, if a child has limited understanding of the situation, it may be extremely difficult for them to make sense of why they are no longer able to see birth relatives and foster carers who have played an important role in their life.

Without the ability to ask questions, they may imagine all sorts of terrible things have happened to their birth family and may undergo a major bereavement; this can seriously inhibit their ability to feel secure in their new family.

When should contact not be considered?

Contact should always be considered, but that does not mean it should always happen. There will be times when a positive decision needs to be made that meetings, telephone calls or the exchange of letters may be detrimental to a child's welfare. This might occur if:

- someone is involved who has previously abused, neglected or failed to protect the child, and it is felt probably that contact will re-awaken fears or such painful memories that the child is re-traumatised;
- the child is unable to feel protected by their permanent family and this undermines the child's ability to settle and feel safe;
- the child is so distressed by contact that this significantly outweighs any long-term benefits that may be accrued;
- the child is exposed to a situation where there is a significant risk that they *will* be harmed by someone.

Deciding that contact is not currently appropriate does not mean that the subject of contact becomes a closed book. It is important to do the following:

- Record why it has been decided that particular types of contact are not appropriate and ensure that the relevant parties are aware of this. This information will then be available for the child at a later date if they have questions about the reasons why contact was stopped.
- Build in reviews so that contact can be re-considered as the child grows up and their circumstances change.
- Consider ways in which information can still be exchanged so that the "door is left open" for the growing child to develop a healthy sense of their identity. This might be through opening a letterbox through an intermediary; the letterbox can lie dormant until all parties feel ready and able to participate. Alternatively, letters and information about the birth family can be kept by the intermediary or by the permanent family until a stage where it is considered that the child feels "safe" enough to see this information.
- Consider whether there is someone else in the birth family who can pass on information. For example, if a child cannot have contact with a sibling who remains in the birth family because this exposes them to too many risks or painful memories, they might be able to receive information from their aunt, for instance, who can reassure them that their sibling is alive and well.

The following case study, taken from Chapter 6 of *See you Soon* (Argent, 1995), explains why contact was ended with a child's father, because it was felt by her mother and other professionals that memories of his formerly abusive behaviour were putting the child at too much risk. It also illustrates the steps the mother took to "keep the door open" for future resumption of her daughter's relationship with her father. Laura's mother sought help for her daughter after it became apparent that her husband had sexually abused the child. The couple separated but after 16 weeks supervised contact was arranged between Laura (aged four) and her father. Although Laura expressed delight at seeing her father and played games with him, she began bedwetting, having nightmares and biting herself (all signs which had first alerted her mother to the fact that abuse had been taking place).

The change in Laura's behaviour was also noted by her nursery school. There was evidence that the behavioural disturbance seriously impeded her capacity to learn and to manage her peer relationships when she was uncharacteristically involved in an aggressive outburst with another child. It seemed clear that contact with her father was profoundly disturbing for her. The recommendation was that contact should be suspended, until she was of an age to protect herself. Indirect contact in the form of letters and cards was managed and supervised by Laura's mother. She regularly writes the required newsletter, enclosing school photos and pictures that Laura wishes to send. All cards and letters received she keeps to give to her daughter when she is older. No requests have been made by Laura to see her father. She understands that he is not seeing her because he hurt her. There are no behavioural disturbances and she is doing well in school and other aspects of her development.

This case is a reminder that, although children may still love relatives who have harmed them, they may be unable to cope with the impact of having contact with them while they are young and vulnerable. They may express their feelings through behaviour rather than words.

Reproduced from *Ten Top Tips for Managing Contact*, by Henrietta Bond, published by BAAF in 2007 (pp 5–13). © Henrietta Bond

Appeasing curiosity and the role of Facebook

A few years ago an 11-year-old girl emailed adoption services, saying that she had been thinking about her birth mother and did not have any information about her and asked if we could send her some information. My manager emailed her back saying we would need to speak to her parents, which we did. Her adoptive parents were very surprised, saying they were open with her. They had received letterbox news from her birth father since her placement, but not the birth mother and her whereabouts were unknown.

Coincidentally, the birth mother contacted me only a few months later to say she was back in the area and asking for help to write a letter and send photos. I contacted the adoptive parents and they agreed. For the last few years we have sent on the birth mother's letters.

Last year I had reason to speak to the adoptive parents with a concern about contact, to be told that they had not shared any of the letters sent by the birth parents with their daughter, now aged nearly 16.

So, even when people say they are open, they are sometimes not, and sometimes they do not understand or want to understand that their children will be curious. I have to question what messages they have been given in their training.

An adoption social worker

Contact with birth relatives

For most adopted children, their birth family will be present in their mind throughout their lives. Sometimes this may be in the forefront and sometimes it may be in the background. The child may think about his birth family in ways that are helpful or unhelpful to him. Direct or indirect forms of contact may facilitate this or not. Just because a child never brings up the subject does not mean that he is not thinking about it or that he won't find himself thinking about it in the future.

- The purpose of contact is not to help or to appease the birth parents – its purpose is primarily to benefit the child.
- In letterbox contact, the adoptive parents write to the child's birth parent, giving them news about the child. The birth parents or other relatives may also write to the adoptive parents. The information is passed through the adoption agency to maintain confidentiality and mediate on any potentially difficult issues.
- The birth parents should not be given any information through the adoption agency that would compromise the adoptive family's anonymity.
- Sometimes there is face-to-face contact between brothers and sisters who are placed in different families, if this is seen as being in the children's best interests. In some placements, there may be face-to-face meetings between the child and birth parent or perhaps a grandparent.
- Contact arrangements are usually made under a voluntary agreement.

It is normal, natural and healthy for adopted children to be curious about their birth parents and their brothers and sisters, to wonder what they are like, and even to wish they could meet them. Sometimes adoptive parents feel hurt or threatened by the child's need to know. Try to remind yourself: *It's not about you.*

Questions of "identity" come sharply into focus as children reach adolescence. All adolescents start to wonder about who they really are, what has shaped them and how others see them. Adopted young people have more questions and experience more confusion than many of their peers because – emotionally – they are members of *two* families. There is a natural urge to find out about their origins and fill in the gaps. This is why life story work that was appropriate when the child was three or four will need to be updated as the child's needs and curiosity develop. Even when they have been told everything that is known about their past, they may still develop a strong need to know what is happening to their birth parents and/or brothers and sisters *now*.

I am aware of one case of a 14-year-old leaving her adoptive home and disappearing to live with her birth father (but in this case I know that the adopters did not respond a few years earlier when she had questions about her birth family, so it could have been curiosity getting the better of her)...Good communication between adopters and their child sounds obvious, but frankly I see cases of children unable to ask poignant questions as their development and understanding increase.
A post-adoption social worker

For young people who were adopted, particularly if they suffered neglect or abuse in early life, the teenage years are often turbulent. Relationships with their adoptive family can become strained, sometimes to breaking point. Just like other teenagers, adopted teenagers test boundaries, can appear to reject their parents, trigger family rows, and feel like running away. But there is an added dimension to all of this for an adopted teenager – the idea that his birth family is somewhere out there.

It was just so easy for our daughter to find her birth parents on Facebook – almost too tempting. It is so easy for children to get on these sites and look for people without really understanding the possible consequences for all involved. Adopted children often have multiple problems, and are often looking for "something else" in their lives, no matter how happy and loved they've been in their adoptive families. Finding their "other" family on Facebook can probably seem like the answer to some of them but will almost certainly cause them much heartache in the long run.
An adoptive mother

It can be important for an adopted child's self-esteem to know that his birth parents care and want to see him.

The fact that my daughter's birth father searched for her meant the world to her – even though he is a schizophrenic who is in secure accommodation and she was told that it would be dangerous for her to have contact with him. There is a powerful pull, particularly in teens, to either make contact or at least get some up-to-date information.

Unattached teens seem to need to make sense of who and why they are as they are, and are usually not getting on well with – or sadly are even estranged from – their adoptive families by that time.

Teenagers (adopted or birth children) who have formed an attachment to their parents "know" they hate their parents, know they will NEVER be like their parents and generally find their parents a pain in the bum…they are secure in all of that. No matter how horrible the teen years may be, they can safely kick against their family, knowing and feeling secure that all will be well and that they "belong".

If only unattached teens could be helped to articulate all their angst and feelings…how different the outcomes could be for them. They make so many mistakes at this time in their life, during a period when they just don't feel like they "belong" anywhere.
An adoptive mother

Why your approach is important

You won't always know if your child has questions about his past or is curious about his birth family. He may keep his questions to himself, either because that's the way he operates or because he thinks you don't want to talk about it or will be angry or hurt.

Sometimes family life gets in the way – the demands of work, school, homework, out-of-school activities and everyone's social lives can crowd other things out. So, if your child doesn't bring it up himself, adoption and birth family can easily become subjects that are never talked about.

A lot of adoptive parents are inhibited when it comes to talking about the child's past. They tend to say, 'My child knows they can ask me anything they want and I'll tell them'. But that may not happen – the child may never ask. Parents understandably push it to the back of their minds.

The importance of openness

We say to parents that, in our experience, every adopted child does think about it.
An adoption social worker

Try to share with your child the letters you receive from his birth parents through letterbox contact, unless there is a good reason not to.

Some parents have a high tolerance threshold for letters that are signed "Mummy" or that say things like "I miss you", while others feel threatened and won't show them to the child.
An adoption social worker

If you are unhappy about the content of the letters, discuss it with the person who manages the letterbox contact.

Many adoptive parents and adoption professionals believe that, if a child has always been able to ask about and discuss and think about what he wants to know about his past, he is less likely to search for information in secret on the internet.

Life story work

Local authorities are required by statutory guidance to include an adopted child's birth parents' first names and the birth family surname in the life story book, so this is standard practice. However, these and other details can allow the child to search for his parents online. Some parents and professionals have anxieties about this, which have led them to feel that practice should change and the child's surname should be kept separately from the life story book rather than in it; that way, parents can gauge the best time to tell the child this. However, others feel that leaving the surname out of the life story book gives the wrong message and will simply make the child more curious about what else is being kept from him. They believe that doing this does not take account of the value to the child of knowing about his past. Each child's case needs to be assessed individually and decisions should be based on the specific details of his family and the circumstances. Decisions on any precautions like this should be proportionate to the risks presented.

Social workers are also required to prepare a "later life letter", which gives a fuller picture of the circumstances which led to the adoption than the simple version in the life story book. This is written with the needs of an older child or adolescent in mind. They give this to the adoptive parents before the adoption order is made. You can give this to your child when you feel the time is right or when he wants more information.

Tell the truth, even if it hurts

Many parents' inclination is to protect their child from the truth about what happened to him in his early years. But – even though parents are acting out of an understandable wish to protect – children have a need to know. They need to be told in a way that is realistic, helpful and supportive. It is an important part of developing an adoption identity.

Exploring the reality of his birth family and the circumstances of his adoption is not something that any child should go through without support. Far better that your child hears the truth from you in the right way rather than discovering it when he finds documents and reports while you're out, goes digging around on the internet, or is told by a birth brother or sister during a secret late-night session on the computer.

The internet is the first point of reference for most young people when there is something they want to know. Young people in Britain turn to the internet to look for help with personal problems rather than seek advice from their parents or friends, according to a survey published in March 2010.

Nine out of 10 of the 1,000 under-25s told the survey for national free helpline Get Connected that they had used the web to search for help in solving a personal problem. Only one-third said they would turn to their mother to discuss a problem, while just one in 20 would speak to their father. Half said they would be likely to speak to a friend.

Children are capable of using the internet to search for information at a young age. This may mean telling your child some things before you would otherwise choose to. How much do you tell? Of course it is not easy to talk to children about the details. It hurts to remind your child of the pain and distress of his early life or in his birth parents' life, or just how he was harmed and by whom. And you will have learned in adoption preparation groups that "demonising" the birth parents could harm the child's self-esteem, given that he is genetically related to them. This sometimes leads adoption workers and adoptive parents to skate over the harsh reality, from the best of motives. The child hears messages like: 'Your parents really loved you, but they couldn't look after you.'

Children who have never known their birth parents sometimes develop an idealised view of them. If they have never been told the facts, when they reach an age when they could seek out and make contact with their birth parents (or be contacted by them), they may be faced with complex and disturbing issues. They may struggle to make sense of what they hear or refuse to believe it.

Some children are sensible and realistic about what they can expect from their birth parents. It helps if you have discussed it openly from an early age, so the birth parents are not surrounded by a sense of mystery and your child will not have a fantasy about what life would have been like with the birth parents.
An adoption social worker

How much you tell and how you phrase it will of course depend on your child's age, but you do need to provide a sensitive, honest and open account of what happened to your child when they were with their birth family.

You are bringing your child up in a loving, safe environment. If he was adopted while very young, a loving, safe environment is all he will be able to remember. When you tell a child 'your parents could not keep you safe', does he really know what that means or what his early life was really like? He may have no real understanding of what you mean. You need to tell them more and more as they get older, and by the time they are teenagers, they need to understand everything.
An adoption social worker

Some adopters struggle with the task of imparting painful and difficult information to their child. For help with this, contact adoption support services and they will be able to advise and support you with finding the best way to talk to your child about his life story and birth family.

There may come a time when your child learns that you have kept certain information from him. Think carefully about any information you are not sharing. One day he may want to know why.

William and his birth brothers

One aspect of William's birth family that we can keep "real" is his two adopted birth brothers. Marc and Luke were adopted by a childless couple in the west of Scotland before we were matched with William. Marc is literally nine months younger than William and Luke is just under twelve months younger than Marc. We met their adoptive parents, Martin and Margaret, at a Christmas social gathering organised by the adoption society which approved us. They have welcomed William warmly into their wider family. We meet up two or three times a year so the children can have time together.

Margaret and Martin are very generous of spirit and shower William with gifts. They include us in family celebrations, such as birthday parties for the boys and other social gatherings. Interestingly, Marc and Luke never ask their parents about their birth family – maybe being brought up together gives them a stronger sense of identity. They do ask about their relationship with our other three children though, all of whom are attentive towards them and are looked up to as really cool, which is good for William to see, given the hard time he still gives them occasionally. Kate in particular has a special place in the eyes of Marc and Luke, as the nearest thing they have to a sister. They look upon the three of them as their adoptive brothers and sister, or cousins, or something in the middle. It doesn't really seem to matter, as long as we explain the relationships as carefully as we can.

It's great seeing William together with Marc and Luke; there's no doubt they have a strong natural bond of blood, though I suspect William's need to assert the bond is stronger than theirs. It's interesting too, that in spite of the attachment, the signs of sibling rivalry between the three of them come quickly to the fore; within an hour William will be telling tales to get one of the others into trouble, and the children will be to-ing and fro-ing to both sets of parents with complaints about each other. It can be hard to maintain the peace. Evie and I sometimes speculate on how the relationships might have been if the boys had all been placed together – the prospect is almost too exhausting to think about – three children born within two years of each other, all with experiences of grief, loss and change, and one with severe disabilities. The contact they have together is demanding for all the parents but worth it, even if it feels a bit frenetic at the time, as if all the bonding as well as the sibling rivalry have to be concentrated into the brief time they are together.

Martin and Margaret agreed to be William's godparents when he was baptised, and that link has helped to bind him to his wider family, and has strengthened his sense of identity and his self-esteem, though just as our family tree is more like a sprawling bush, our adoption triangle is more of a polygon. We have Marc and Luke to stay over on their own occasionally and William has been to stay with them too. It makes for complicated class discussions at school, when the children are invited to share their news after the weekend. One of William's classmates once accosted me in the playground when I went to collect him at the end of the day, to demand that I refute William's assertion that he'd been to see some mysterious younger brothers the day before. Whilst we are open about William's adoption, there are times when it would be good just to have a bit more privacy. But William has to feel able to share who he is, and he's certainly not bashful about it!

* * *

Adopted children have birth families out there somewhere. There may be direct contact with them, indirect contact (through the exchange of photographs or letters) or no contact. Even if there is no contact, the birth family is part of the child's identity, and adoptive parents need to be able to feel comfortable in handling questions from the child about their other family. Contact, or even talking about the birth family, can trigger all sorts of mixed feelings in the child, and the fallout, distress and anger can last for days. It is generally healthier to allow the child to express these real feelings than to suppress them. Adopted children can build up rosy fantasies about their birth families. If there is direct contact, the child, the adopters and the birth family should be offered professional support.

Who am I?

Alison Langford

Alison Langford was born in 1936 in the north-east of England as the result of an affair between her mother (white British) and a married man (unknown). She went to her adoptive family when she was five months old. She employed a tracing agency four years ago and has found that she is part of a very large family. Alison is in touch with five cousins and has been warmly accepted by them. One dear old lady of 96 remembers Alison's mother with affection, which is very special, and she has been given some wonderful old photos. Alison has lived in Surrey ever since her adoption and has been happily married for 48 years, but has no children. It was therefore doubly important for her to find her roots. This poem was previously published in an issue of the Surrey Adoptee Support Group newsletter.

I wondered where I came from
To whom did I belong?
No father named
My mother shamed
But I had done no wrong.
In childhood games
I wondered why

I never felt the same.
No siblings, too, to talk it through
Plus a new rootless name.
When starting work
The questions asked
Upset me till I cried.
What illnesses and problems were
And when my mother died?
On marriage I acquired a name
That had some real meaning.
But still no blood relations
For whom I'd have strong feeling.
When no child came
I thought that this was going to be my lot.
Although I'd much to thank God for
I thought that He'd forgot
How much I want identity
Not just a blob in space.
A real place in history
To join the human race.
Imagine my delight
When at last I had a plan
To search for my relations
By whatever means I can.
I'd left it rather late to try
As I am growing old.
Some folk are not alive now.
The clues are going cold.
However, with the help of Jane
And website information
Cousins I've found
Joy all around
With many generations.
So now at last I've found the past
Believe it if you can.
And I am just a tiny cog
In a gi-normous clan!

Reproduced from *Chosen*, edited by Perlita Harris, published by BAAF in 2012 (pp 45–46). © BAAF

Contact is really important

Georgie (age 11)

My sister and I are allowed to write a letter to our mum every year. When the time comes to write it is very exciting. We write about all our news. I love the day we get a letter back from our mum. I feel very excited waiting for the letter. It's a shame we only get to write once a year because I have lots of news I could tell my mum. I only get to write once a year because the judge said so. I think the judge's decision that we can't meet until I am an adult was a good idea. If I did meet her it would mix with my life now and make my life complicated and make me feel pulled in two directions.

We are allowed to meet our brother. I get to see him once or twice a year because we live in different countries. I love seeing him. I feel very happy and excited when we are going to meet. It's like seeing a long lost friend. I love the excitement of meeting him at the door. When we are together we go to the park, to the shops or to the cinema. Mostly we just play games like spies or pirates. We all sleep in the same room and play a game where we have to roll over each other – it keeps us awake for hours. I hate leaving or seeing him leave but there is always the chance that our parents will get distracted and we get another half an hour together. I miss my brother but I don't cry. We phone each other quite often. My sister always pulls faces when I am on the phone to him because she wants me to finish so she can have a chat.

I feel contact is really important. There's no point in hiding the fact that you have another mother in the world because some day you'll meet her again. It's important to know about her and what she is doing. It's important not to hide your emotions because if you do some day they will all come out together and you might feel depressed.

I don't have contact with my dad. I never knew him – I can't remember him. I didn't even see a photo of him until I was nine. I asked my mum if she had a photo and she got in touch with him and got me two photos. Seeing the photos didn't really have a big effect on me. I was curious to see what he looked like and to see if he looked like me. I was a little disappointed that we didn't look like each other. I wonder if my dad is in any way like me in personality. I would like to get in touch with him – maybe a letter each year. I think some of the other people in my past life weren't the nicest people so I don't want them to have anything to do with me again or to have them in my life.

If I was given a choice about contact I would find it very tricky. I'd love to meet my mum but then it would be scary because I'd feel torn. It's a difficult thing to think about and I have no idea what I would decide if I was given the choice. I think different things different days. I think life is nicer and easier for me because my mum and my parents are in contact too. They write letters to each other. My parents think my mum is a very nice person. If they didn't write I'd feel upset because I'd think that they didn't like each other and were jealous of each other. My parents met my mum and we have a photo of them together. I think both my mums will be great friends when we meet again.

Reproduced from *The Colours in Me*, edited by Perlita Harris, published by BAAF in 2008 (p 134). © BAAF

MODULE 9: **Life as an adoptive family – learning to live together**

Learning outcomes

This module aims to help you to:

- **think about what early days with your adopted child might bring**
- **consider behavioural strategies children may have developed to survive past abuse and/or neglect**
- **know more about your likely need for support and how you can access this**
- **consider the needs of an adopted child in school**

UNDERSTANDING THE EFFECTS OF TRAUMA

Charlie's world had been about survival

One of the 24 Ss that Dan Hughes refers to earlier in this book is 'Seeking the meaning of the behaviour'; this process can often be helped by looking at the "paperwork" for the child or talking to their social worker, to gain an understanding of the child's life story. We have found the following questions useful to help us to understand what is going on.

1. What do we know about the child's past, that may explain the behaviour and be their motivator?

2. Have they been "taught" to behave in this way and believe it to be normal?

3. Could maintaining the behaviour be an important way to stay loyal to their family?

4. Is the "story" we are being told completely fictitious or could elements of it be true, with bits added to make it more acceptable?

5. Has the child rehearsed the story in their mind so often that they believe it is true?

6. What consequence might they fear if we find out the truth?

7. Are they using the behaviour to confirm feelings of worthlessness or a core belief – "I am bad"?

8. Are they using the behaviour to create an atmosphere in the house they are familiar with? Predictable negative responses from adults can be better than unpredictable positive ones. A turbulent environment can feel familiar and safer than an unfamiliar calm atmosphere.

9. Are they using the behaviour to get back at the world?

10. Are our own responses and reactions feeding the situation?

Like many children who are in care, Charlie's world had been about survival. His mum's drug and alcohol problems resulted in there often not being any food to eat. It had become Charlie's role to ensure that the family had food on the table, and he was rewarded by his mum with sweets when his forays were successful. Sweets became a safety net and currency for Charlie. If he couldn't steal something from a lunchbox, most of the children at his school who had packed lunches were willing to swap a sandwich for sweets, and if later in the day Charlie discovered that the cupboards at home were bare, the sandwich was better than nothing. Perhaps a sandwich could be used to appease an angry parent? If Charlie had sweets he was safe. Also associated with rewards, they had become a symbol of success and a sweet in his mouth allowed

157

him to have a rare moment when he felt good about himself.

What seemed like ridiculous food to hoard in a bedroom – cheese, ham and other items – were literally survival rations for Charlie. He had no idea about "sell by dates", refrigeration and the like, he just knew that there could be times when he wouldn't be able to steal enough food for the day or that what he did steal would be eaten by one of his "dads" and he needed to know that he had something in reserve.

Eating the other children's "leftovers" at school, even though he wasn't hungry, was another way of making sure he had enough to eat that day, in case nothing was available later. He was eating far more than was healthy for him in his quest not to feel hungry, for being hungry reminded him of his difficult circumstances.

Charlie knew that his family wasn't like most of his friends' families, and so lying about the reality seemed like the only option to him. Like the lies he needed to tell his mum, or the men in her life, if he returned home with no food. Perhaps lies were the only defence available to protect himself from abusive punishment, ridicule and humiliation, all of which confirmed that he was "bad". Lies were needed for self-preservation and, like stealing, had become a part of Charlie's behaviour in order for him to survive.

The motivation behind Charlie's behaviour was not unusual; we have cared for children who have spoken about stealing newspapers from letterboxes, hubcaps and other automobilia, money or electronic devices, and often selling them on the streets to buy food or even fund their parents' addictions. A mum on drugs can be safer to live with than one suffering from withdrawal symptoms. Again, it all boils down to self-preservation and results in the child developing a completely different moral compass from that of most people.

Reproduced from an account by Lorna Miles in *Parenting a Child with Emotional and Behavioural Difficulties*, by Dan Hughes, published by BAAF in 2012 (pp 71–72). © Lorna Miles

The neurobiology of child mental disorders and stress

(This chapter draws on Glaser D (2000) 'Child abuse and neglect and the brain: a review', *Journal of Child Psychology & Psychiatry*, 41:1, pp 97–116.)

We know that the lack of a warm, positive relationship with their primary caregiver and insecure attachment are strongly linked with subsequent behavioural and emotional problems in the child.

It may be helpful to understand the physiological processes that can explain why a child expresses the effects of abusive or traumatic experiences through mental health or behavioural disorders.

Neurobiologists have been researching what might be happening in a child's brain to drive these behaviours, with a particular emphasis on the physiological effects of stress. This research is still in its infancy and much is conjecture, for obvious reasons – it is impossible to know for certain what is happening inside a living child's brain. Much of the current theory is built on experimentation with animals.

The child's brain

A child's brain is very sensitive and very plastic (malleable), particularly in the first two years of life, when it undergoes a massive amount of development in a very short period of time. In normal, healthy child-rearing, the parents/caregiver will have a huge amount of interaction with the child. This interaction, often called "serve and return", stimulates the brain to form the synaptic connections in the frontal lobe that become the framework for the child's lifelong cognitive capacity and behaviour. The child does something, and the parent responds, and vice versa, as in a tennis game. These interactions should be sensitive, nurturing and predictable; the child should be protected from fear and stress, and from too much sensory input, and gently encouraged and supported to explore new things. If the child is secure in the knowledge that their parent is there to provide comfort, safety and reassurance, then the child will be securely attached.

Neglected and abused children do not have these kinds of interactions with their parent. Nor do they have the security of a safe base from which to explore the world and new experiences. This means the synaptic connections in their brain are not stimulated, which means the cognitive framework is not built. Parts of the brain may even die off, leaving (famously in the case of abandoned children found in Romania's orphanages after the fall of Ceausescu in 1989) a "black hole" in the frontal lobe – the part of the brain concerned with emotions, behaviour and cognition.

The frontal lobe is more highly developed in humans than in other mammals. This is the part of the brain that gives us the capacity to think ahead, to be aware of consequences of our actions, to build relationships with other people and to feel kindness, empathy and concern. It enables us to be self-aware, to solve problems, to be creative and to use our imagination. It also helps us to regulate our own emotions so that we can calm ourselves when we feel stressed.

These functions don't develop until the end of the first year of a child's life. A child who does not have a nurturing relationship with their parent does not learn how to express their emotions or how to regulate their stress levels by themselves.

When the role of this part of the brain and its importance in early childhood development are understood, it is easier to see why some adopted children from abusive families or families with a history of mental disorder or substance misuse behave as they do, and can struggle throughout life, despite a subsequent nurturing upbringing.

The brain of a child who is neglected, abused and/or under-stimulated in these early years will remain under-developed, leaving the child less able to learn and less likely to achieve their full potential and develop good social skills. It can also mean they behave in unusual and often anti-social ways, because those parts of their brain that govern social behaviours and emotions are under-developed, or simply not there.

Neurobiologists theorise that an abused, mistreated child will not be able to regulate their emotional responses to stressful situations. Their brain will not have the capacity to do so, resulting in inappropriate and difficult behaviours and, ultimately, mental disorders. The longer the child is exposed to abusive or neglectful parenting, the more difficult it will be to recover the lost connections in their brain. The child may be taught in later life, using cognitive behavioural techniques, how to behave and respond in certain situations, but they will lack the seemingly automatic and instinctive response of the child brought up in a safe and nurturing environment.

Stress

Neurobiologists are also making important discoveries about the physiological mechanisms of the human stress response system.

A small amount of stress is a good thing: it is a normal human response to the new, the unfamiliar and the unexpected. It heightens our senses. At its most basic, it enables us to "fight or flee" threat or danger. But when the stress is repeated, persistent and long term, without relief, it becomes literally toxic, and can lead to damage to parts of the brain, as well as major physical and mental health problems (including high risk of coronary heart disease and mental ill health such as depression) in adult life.

The stress response is the body's way of coping with frightening, unexpected and abusive situations. It is highly complex. Put very simply, it involves the hypothalamic-pituitary-adrenal (HPA) axis – the pathway connecting the brain to the adrenal cortex, which secretes the stress hormone cortisol into the blood stream. When cortisol is produced in response to exposure to stressful or frightening situations, it suppresses the body's immune response, increases the levels of glucose in the blood stream and dampens the fear response. These all improve the body's ability to deal with the threat.

This system is self-regulating, in that when certain parts of the brain register that the amount of cortisol in the blood stream has risen, they send a message via the HPA axis to the adrenal cortex to reduce the levels, so the body is not flooded with damaging amounts of cortisol and can return to homeostasis (this would be like taking the foot off the accelerator in a stationary car, so the engine returns to normal, idling state). If increased levels of cortisol are still required (for example, in situations of extreme danger, requiring extra energy and strength), this too can be communicated to the HPA axis. Cortisol levels normally fluctuate over the course of the day – they are higher in the morning and reduce in the afternoon.

Another response to stress is certain kinds of behaviour. Interestingly, cortisol levels and these behaviours do not necessarily coincide. At age two to six months a child's raised cortisol levels and crying in response to fear or pain will be about equal. But in a healthy child at 15 months, crying will exceed the levels of cortisol. Studies have also found that giving a child a dummy will stop the crying behaviour, but the levels of cortisol will remain unaffected – the equivalent to the body's engine continuing to accelerate hard, even though the car is not moving.

Raised cortisol levels can be harmful to brain development. In particular, they affect the hippocampus. This is the part of the brain concerned with verbal and visual memory. High exposure to cortisol leads to hippocampal cell death.

Studies both of humans and animals show that reassuring, nurturing contact with the mother restores levels of cortisol to normal levels. Specifically, studies show that insecurely attached children are much more likely than securely attached children to have high levels of cortisol in their system when exposed to frightening situations. Children with a disorganised/disoriented attachment style are particularly vulnerable to raised cortisol levels when exposed to situations that securely attached children find only slightly scary.

Long-term exposure to stress has been found to lead to positive and withdrawn behaviour ("learned hopelessness"), which neurobiologists explain as the body's attempt to control the flood of cortisol within normal, manageable limits.

Another important part of the body's stress response system is the adrenal gland. This secretes adrenaline and noradrenaline, which increase the heart rate and blood pressure, cause sweating and activate the body's "fight or flight" response to stress. Persistent and repeated raised levels of these hormones may be linked to the impulsive behaviour and short attention span associated with ADHD.

The difficult behaviours of abused children can thus be described in terms of the body's physiological responses to extended and repeated stress, and the excess release of adrenaline and cortisol.

Research suggests that exposure to adverse environments and abuse has a greater effect than genetic vulnerability or resilience.

The good news is that early intervention to remove the child from the source of stress and provide safety and reassurance can prevent long-term damage to his or her mental health and wellbeing.

Reproduced from *Parenting a Child with Mental Health Issues*, by Catherine Jackson, published by BAAF in 2012 (pp 48–53). © Catherine Jackson

My story

Jane (age 17)

My name is Jane. I have Foetal Alcohol Syndrome. I have it because my mother was an alcoholic. My speech, hearing, auditory processing, my heart and stomach were affected. I spent a month in intensive care with projectile vomiting, bowel infection and a heart murmur. I had an operation to stop the vomiting and get rid of the bowel infection. The heart murmur went away when I was five. I was a very small baby due to my mother's drinking; I am still quite short for my age. My jaw and teeth were also affected; my teeth were very twisted.

I am healthy now but the long-lasting effect has been on my brain. My auditory processing is very slow and I also have trouble with my memory. This means that I can only follow one instruction at a time and I often quickly forget what I'm supposed to be doing. I only hear one in three words so I take a long time to respond. This means friendships are difficult because I have trouble following a group conversation.

This means I also have trouble at school and with learning. Trying to follow a teacher's conversation is difficult. I often get the wrong idea of what I'm learning and my homework. I need help with note-taking because I'm not fast enough to write it all down before the teacher goes on to the next thing. I need one-to-one conversation with the teacher so I can understand what I'm doing. After a psychologist who understands Foetal Alcohol Syndrome tested me, he wrote a report for the teachers and they were able to help me much better. I also had learning support workers in some of my lessons. When I was younger I had speech therapy and later I had special listening from a private SpLD [Specific Learning Difficulty] teacher. At primary school I was told off a lot for doing things I shouldn't because I hadn't heard what the teacher said. In the morning before school I used to stand by myself because I didn't know how to socialise and approach people and the other kids found me difficult to talk to.

Secondary school was the same because I had the same problems so I was often on my own so people started to bully me and call me names because they thought I was weird because I was usually on my own. If people asked me to sit with them at lunch I would stay by myself. Because I felt very unsafe and tense around new people and I felt safer by myself, though it made me very lonely.

Though I wanted to be with them I never felt like I fitted in because I was quiet because I wasn't good at socialising with new people. Sometimes people would tease me because I took a long time to respond or I hadn't heard what the person had said so they thought I was not clever.

Now I'm at college doing animal care and I get the right sort of help straight away so work is easier. I also have made some friends.

Reproduced from *The Colours in Me*, edited by Perlita Harris, published by BAAF in 2008 (p 41). © BAAF

SUPPORT FOR FAMILIES

Understanding Jack's learning difficulty

Jack's schoolwork has improved slightly during his three years with us. He can concentrate better and does read a bit, but should be achieving more. No one had been able to pinpoint why he wasn't learning until a few weeks ago, when he told me how his birth father physically threatened him when he was unable to remember his letters and numbers. He is afraid that a mistake will put his life in danger. Every time he tries to read he has to cope with all the feelings his birth father aroused in him. So we are going back to see Joy in the hope that she can release him from his terror and, who knows, that may help his learning difficulties.

For me, every aspect of therapy has been worth it because of all the support and practical advice we have had. Joy was able to explain behaviour that seemed outrageous and beyond our understanding. Initially we participated in the boys' therapy sessions, but more lately Ed and I have attended workshops organised by Joy and her team. These have proved invaluable because so much has been discovered about trauma and how it affects a child's development generally, and more specifically, the infant brain; how the effects of emotional neglect and abuse disable a child from using this most vital part of their body. It relegates parts of their brain to a wheelchair, disables them intellectually as with Jack, or emotionally, as with Joe.

Managing behaviour and emotions

Like any adopted child, Scott has attachment issues. Early on, the slightest thing would affect him deeply. He would be quick to fly off the handle and get over-excited or very angry and it was difficult to get him back to normal. I went online and looked at parenting forums and devised a strategy to help him. He used to scream before leaving for school but now I know better how to manage his behaviour and emotions. We know the likely flashpoints and are much calmer. It is important for him not to feel abandoned, so if he has to have time out we sit with him. We also try to encourage eye contact and have some exercises to help with this. When he was younger, he would sit on our laps facing us and we would feed him and let him grab our noses – this encouraged him to look at our faces and give eye contact.

Part of our strategy is being very clear about what is happening in the day and having rules. We have a noticeboard in the kitchen with family rules like: put shoes on quickly when asked, no screaming, no hitting and be nice to each other. Children respond well to rules.

We had some attachment therapy, organised through Social Services, which was a great help. It would be useful to be able to call an expert sometimes to get advice – it would be good if post-adoption support was clearer.

Scott relies on us more and more as a source of consolation, whereas at first he would run away when he was hurt. It was really nice when he first sought us for solace. Now he asks to snuggle up, whereas before he used to put his knees or something else between us.

Apparently, seven is a crucial age in terms of attachment so we may need more help, but I think Scott is going to be OK as he has shown he can build meaningful relationships.

Tips on supporting adopted children in school

- When the child moves in with adopters it is best if he can start in his new school at the start rather than in the middle of term.
- Adopters should be aware that lessons on certain subjects could be upsetting for the child, for example, being asked to bring in a photograph of himself as a baby (he may not have any); to write an autobiography; to write an essay entitled "My family"; or to design a family tree.
- Lessons on genetics, sex education and drugs education may remind a child or young person (e.g. one who has been sexually abused or whose birth parents misused drugs) of behaviour of birth relatives. A child who has suffered sexual abuse may be much more knowledgeable than his/her peers and make inappropriate comments in lessons, or may be upset by the lesson's content.
- For a child who has suffered many losses in his life, a favourite teacher or close friend leaving

the school can be particularly hard and may rekindle memories of past losses.

- The child may be unsure of how or how much to tell his schoolmates about his past or his adoption. He may share too much and then find that they fail to respect confidences or use the information to bully him.
- Certain things in school might trigger traumatic memories. For instance, for a child who has been sexually abused, showering after PE might be frightening.
- Refer to the section in this module on social networking. For older children, social networking might compromise confidentiality of placement.

When living or working with a traumatised child, the issue is not "what to do" but rather "how to be". A calm teacher who expresses his or her own feelings appropriately and stays in control of the emotional tone of the environment can create a feeling of safety and security, which will help to soothe the child's hyperarousal, fear or anger.

Of course, there may be times when a child or young person has to leave the classroom because their behaviour is unacceptably disruptive or because they are putting themselves or others at risk. The school will have a protocol for dealing with incidents like this, which will involve removing the child from the classroom and sending him to someone else, so that the teacher can continue to teach the rest of the class. In the case of a traumatised child, this protocol should ideally acknowledge and address the child's difficulties and should aim to help him to learn from the incident.

Adapted from *Ten Top Tips for Supporting Education* (Fursland et al, 2013, pp 69–70). © Eileen Fursland *et al*

ON PARENTING

The adoption of children with disabilities

When Evie and I got married, one of our friends gave us a spoof wedding present of a little paperback book called *Tips and Wrinkles*. It has a subtitle: *A treasury of ways to save time and money around the home*. It contains all sorts of indispensable advice such as: 'To "iron" a handkerchief in an emergency, ease it out flat while still wet on a mirror or on the glass of a picture and leave until dry.' We've yet to encounter an emergency requiring an ironed hankie. We gave up ironing hankies years ago. The book quotes the definition of a "wrinkle" as 'a piece of information not generally known'.

This chapter contains tips and wrinkles about the adoption of children with disabilities. However, each adoption journey is different, just as each child is different. All advice and information therefore needs to be taken with a large pinch of salt, but here goes!

When I trained as a social worker in the dim and distant past, nearly all children "put up" for adoption were healthy babies. Older children and children with disabilities were generally brought up by foster carers or in care homes or institutions. Things have changed a lot. There are relatively few babies "available" for adoption these days; lone parents are supported to care for their children, contraception is freely available, and illegitimacy is no longer a disgrace.

Nowadays, the children who need adoptive families are older; they may have suffered neglect or abuse or they may be disabled. They may have had a number of periods in care, and might find it difficult to form attachments. They can have behavioural or emotional problems that may last for years.

At the same time, there is no longer a stereotypical adoptive family. Adopters might be childless or they might have other children. They might be married, living with a partner, divorced, single, in same sex relationships, disabled, and from any racial, ethnic or religious background. And applicants don't need to be in the first flush of youth. The assessment of potential adopters now involves training, usually in a group setting, and a home study, which will focus particularly on gathering evidence to show that the applicants will make good enough parents. There are lots of children waiting for adoption and they don't need perfect parents!

You can't adopt on top of everything else you do – something will have to go. Children with disabilities take a lot of care and time. Try drawing a circle and dividing it into segments – each segment representing the amount of time you spend on the different things you do: stamp collecting, windsurfing, clay pigeon shooting, watching soaps or whatever. What are you prepared to give up in order to insert a large new childcare segment?

Our experience of being assessed and trained as adoptive parents was positive. It is important not to feel that you are being judged, but to use the process as an opportunity to learn, and a chance to work out whether adoption is for you. We know a number of people who have gone through the process and who have finally decided against adoption, but who have still found the experience personally valuable.

Once you reach the stage of being "matched" with a child, it is important to get as much information as you can before making a final commitment to proceed. However, William in the flesh was not the same as William in the pictures, or in the reports we'd read, and living with William was different again. Diagnoses and prognoses are useful up to a point, but labels are not, and it is important to have an open mind. We had thought William would eventually be able to walk using a frame, and then had to get used to the idea that this was not going to happen.

Adoptive parents get to know children in a way that others have not been able to. This might be stating the obvious: of course parents should know their children best! But it can lead to surprises and shocks. I know adoptive parents who have found out from their children that they have been sexually abused in the past, something that had not been known beforehand. It may be that children only feel able to make such disclosures from within the security of a "forever" family.

The first few months or years of caring for an adopted child can be particularly challenging. At the point of placement the child will be experiencing change and loss. They might be "testing" their new parents; the family might not be quite what they were expecting; they will have mixed feelings. Try putting yourself in their shoes for a while. Adoption is not often a soft-focused Anne of Green Gables story, either for the child or the adopters. But ultimately, most adoptions are successful in the grossly generalised meaning of the word.

Don't expect too much of yourself as an adoptive parent! You will probably feel that you aren't doing enough to help the child realise his or her full potential, or that despite all your best efforts, the child doesn't give much back, doesn't appreciate you and says cruel things to you. You can only do what you can do. It can be difficult to notice progress on a day-to-day basis; try to have six monthly reviews, whether formally with those involved in the child's care, health and education, or informally with friends and family, so you can acknowledge and mark progress.

Adopted children have birth families out there somewhere. There may be direct contact with them, indirect contact (through the exchange of photographs or letters) or no contact. Even if there is no contact, the birth family is part of the child's identity, and adoptive parents need to be able to feel comfortable in handling questions from the child about their other family. Contact, or even talking about the birth family, can trigger all sorts of mixed feelings in the child, and the fallout, distress and anger can last for days. It is generally healthier to allow the child to express these real feelings than to suppress them. Adopted children can build up rosy fantasies about their birth families. If there is direct contact, the child, the adopters and the birth family should be offered professional support.

Much of the support Evie and I get for managing "the Family Business" comes from each other. It is essential to talk to your partner about how you feel, and about all the little problems that will arise each day. If you haven't got a partner, choose a special friend.

As a parent you can expect to lose your temper and to be grumpy and nag, but try and de-brief yourself afterwards, and talk it over with the child. If criticism of children who have been brought up in a *secure* environment from birth is to be effective, it needs to be balanced with praise. As a rule of thumb, one critical comment needs to be offset by three positive ones. So, 'Charlie, you've left your shoes in the middle of the floor *again*,' only has a chance of making an impression if you balance it with, say, 'Thanks, Charlie, for clearing your plate away – that's really helpful,' *and* 'you got on with your homework really quickly today,' *and* 'I really enjoyed going shopping with you today, Charlie!' Adopted children need at least *six* statements of praise for each criticism. Some say they need as many as twenty! Incessant nagging doesn't work, but it's easier said than done.

In our admittedly very limited experience, children with disabilities have all the same emotional problems as other adopted children, including loss, disrupted attachment and poor self-esteem. These can be just as hard to deal with as the disability itself.

We have found that William glows with pleasure if he can get a sense of achievement from doing something. For example, he can swim a little, ride his trike and work the computer. It's important to keep trying to find new, stimulating activities for children with limited abilities. We recently entombed some new mysterious toy knights in a block of plaster of Paris and William excavated them using my hammer. It took him two days to complete the job and afterwards there was plaster ground into all his clothes, but it gave him a real sense of satisfaction, and helped his co-ordination and concentration skills.

If you have more than one child, make sure you give each one some individual time. This might seem fairly obvious, but it is easy to get into a routine revolving around the family group and the disabled child, and everyone needs some one-to-one time, though my older children suddenly seem to have something urgent to do when I suggest a walk or try to recruit one of them to help me to cook the dinner.

If you're not naturally assertive, go to classes! You need to be able to speak up for your child, sometimes in intimidating settings. Rehearse what you want to say before you go to the meeting. We have also found it very helpful to have an ally in some meetings. The worker at our local Princess Royal Trust Carers' Centre has been particularly good at advocating our needs and William's needs at various review meetings. Her experience, knowledge and dispassionate objectivity shine through.

Unless you are one of those serene, unflappable types, take up yoga as an aid to maintaining your cool. If you haven't time for yoga, counting to ten, slowly, is a fair substitute when you're feeling stressed. Adopting a child with disabilities is hard work. Take all the financial, practical and emotional help you are offered and then ask for more! It took us ages to find out about financial help and benefits that can be available. It's way beyond the scope of this book to give a comprehensive directory of relevant legislation and sources of help and support, but some of the following clues might point you in the right direction. Access to a computer with internet and a search engine is just about essential. Do as much research as possible *before* the child arrives.

Legislation about adoption is changing and is different in Scotland, England and Wales and Northern Ireland. Make sure you are clear about the legal status of the child and the court procedures that might lie ahead. Check how the costs of any legal processes will be met. There should be a post-placement adoption plan for the child, setting down what support you can expect from the local authority that "looked after" the child. Once the adoption has been finalised, the local authority where you live (which might be different from the one that placed the child) should not discriminate against you or the child because the child is adopted. Try and get the placing local authority to be clear about which authority is responsible for what from the outset.

If you adopt a child with additional needs, he or she might attract an *adoption allowance*. This is payable by the local authority which had legal responsibility for the child prior to placement, and payments can continue for as long as the child remains in full-time education. The criteria for an allowance are complex, but roughly speaking require that the child will incur care costs which will be greater than for other children, and that adoption would not be practicable without the payment of an allowance. Applicants are means tested, and adoption allowance schemes can vary between local authorities, so that a child might attract an allowance in one part of the country, but not in another.

There are a number of national and local organisations that provide advice and support to adopters. Support can include counselling, training and mutual support groups for adopters and their children. You should be able to find details on the internet. Some of the organisations are run by adopters.

Local authorities have a number of duties and powers in relation to children with disabilities. Again, some of the legislation in Scotland is different from that in England and Wales and

Northern Ireland. As a common principle, local authorities have statutory duties to assess the needs of disabled people for support and services. Disabled people should be entitled to an assessment of their needs in respect of:

- practical assistance in the home, such as domiciliary care;
- assistance in taking advantage of educational facilities;
- transport to and from home in relation to certain services;
- aids and adaptations – we have had help with the costs of installing a downstairs shower room and have been offered help with a ramp up to the front door;
- assistance with holidays;
- dietary requirements;
- assistance in obtaining a telephone. A social worker, occupational therapist or care manager from the social services or social work department usually carries out assessments.

Sometimes there can be quite a wait to get an assessment. Local authorities have finite budgets and are not always able to provide what has been assessed as needed. There are complaints and appeals procedures if you are dissatisfied with the service, or lack of it.

Children affected by disability may be subject to a number of other statutory assessments, and local authorities should try to complete these concurrently or combine them. These assessments can be difficult for parents to respond to, not only because of the inherent labelling of the child, but also because of the seeming judgements that are made by people who have minimal contact with your child.

People with disabilities (or their carers) can apply for *direct payments*, now sometimes called "self-directed support" (just when you get used to one form of terminology, they change it), to employ carers or pay for care agencies privately. The idea behind this is to empower people with disabilities and their carers to make their own arrangements, in ways that can be closely tailored to their needs. We have enquired about direct payments in relation to William a number of times, but have been advised that there are no funds available.

The law relating to the education of children with disabilities varies depending on which part of the UK you live in. Education authorities in the UK now generally accept the principle of "inclusion". New laws mean schools, colleges and universities cannot treat disabled students "less favourably" than non-disabled students. And they must make "reasonable adjustments" to ensure disabled students are not disadvantaged compared to their non-disabled peers. These new laws cover school admissions, exclusions and education and associated services, including school trips and after-school clubs and activities.

Schools and local authorities must now also draw up strategic plans to make it easier for disabled pupils to be taught in mainstream schools. They must:

- improve physical access to buildings with ramps, handrails and lifts;
- make lessons more accessible through staff training and class organisation;
- make information more easily available through handouts and timetables in large print, Braille or audio tape.

There are still lots of specialist schools for children with disabilities. Parents, children and educationalists can have different views, often strongly held, about whether inclusion or specialism is better. The education authority/department will assess the child's needs, usually with the involvement of an educational psychologist. There are appeals procedures if parents and children disagree with the local authority about the provision that is offered. There are advocacy and mediation services to help and support parents with this process. Each child with additional needs should have a co-ordinated education support plan, or its equivalent, and this plan should be reviewed regularly.

There are a number of state benefits for children with disabilities that are the same all over the UK. A *Disability Living Allowance* (DLA) might be payable if the disabled person has needed help for three months and is likely to need assistance for at least a further six months. There are two components to DLA. The Care Component can be claimed for a child of any age who requires special personal care or help with communicating. It can also be paid for deaf or visually impaired children or for a child who needs someone to be with them in order to stop them hurting themelves or other people. There are specfic criteria for children who are terminally ill. The Mobility Component can be claimed for a child over three who is unable to walk or has difficulty walking because of their disability, or for children over five if they can walk, but need someone with them to ensure they are safe or to help them find their way around. DLA is paid on behalf of the child and is not means tested.

Parents of adopted children are entitled to *child benefit*, the same as other parents. A *Carer's Allowance* may be payable to adopters on a low income who look after a person over the age of 16 with an illness or disability, who is not in full-time education. Increased levels of *Child Tax Credit* are payable to people with children who have disabilities, depending on their income.

The Family Fund Trust is a government-funded charity which provides money to buy equipment or services for children with disabilities. Applicants are means tested. There are other charitable Trusts that give funds for specialist equipment, holidays and activities for disabled children. It is sometimes possible to access assistance even if you have a reasonably good income.

A *disabled parking badge* (Blue Badge) can be issued by the local authority. Children can be eligible if they have mobility problems or are registered blind. But don't forget to renew it as it is not given for life and there is no reminder!

People, including children, claiming the higher rate of the mobility component of DLA can be exempted from road tax, but the vehicle must be used only for the disabled person.

If your home has been adapted to meet the needs of a disabled person, you may be eligible for a reduction in council tax.

If your child is registered blind you may get a 50 per cent reduction in the cost of a TV licence. In most parts of the country disabled children and their attendant can get free transport on local buses. There may be concessions on rail travel, certain ferries and toll bridges.

There is a national network of accessible public toilets, for which it is necessary to buy a key. Evie has a mini unpublicised campaign to use the term "accessible" in relation to toilets/parking spaces/buses, etc, because if they were "disabled" as they are often labelled, they might not work particularly well! You can get a bit touchy when you're in the disability world.

Many local and national organisations provide services to families with disabled children. Contact a Family is a national charity which offers support and advice to parents whose children have special needs or disabilities, regardless of their particular medical condition. Their website has a directory of specific conditions and rare syndromes and they specialise in putting families in touch with each other.

The disability world has a dizzying array of professionals with whom you may be in contact at some stage. Here are a few of the main ones and a summary of their roles.

Occupational therapists (OTs) are trained to look at how to maximise self-help. They can provide appropriate equipment and adaptations to the home and can advise and help people with disabilities to adapt to their environment. OTs can be based in health departments or local authorities and work in a variety of settings: child development centres, nurseries, schools (mainstream and special schools), at home or in hospitals. Examples of the help we have had from OTs include adaptations to the home and aids to daily living, such as special cutlery that is easy to hold, toilet seating, devices to help transfer from wheelchair to bed and so on.

Paediatric physiotherapists are concerned with the assessment, treatment and management of children who have a general developmental delay, mobility disorder, disability or illness which may be improved, controlled or alleviated by physiotherapy and/or the use of specialised equipment. In our experience, the physiotherapy service can be very stretched, and the amount of direct contact may therefore be limited. Physiotherapists can be helpful in devising exercise programmes to counter the effects of progressive conditions and to develop mobility skills. They can provide equipment, such as walking frames, to aid mobility.

The *Speech and Language Therapy Service* aims to promote the child's communication and/or eating and drinking skills. Therapists can offer advice and assistance in relation to problems of swallowing and drooling. Children can access this therapy from birth, for example, if a child is born with a cleft palate, or has eating/drinking difficulties, or Down's syndrome.

Community and hospital-based *audiometricians* work with paediatricians in assessing hearing impairment.

The *Community Paediatric Service* undertakes medical assessments of children with developmental, behavioural or learning difficulties that may have an underlying medical cause. Community paediatricians provide advice and support to parents, young people, teachers and a wide range of professionals working in other agencies. The range and number of therapists and others will vary depending on the nature your child's disability. It is worth trying to build good relations with them (we are all human) and choosing one or two who can act as "key workers" and who might help to co-ordinate services.

If you become the parent of a disabled child, you will come across physical barriers, social injustices and obstacles to the inclusion of your child in all sorts of ways. You are likely to get cross and frustrated and to want to change things. There are both national and local campaign groups, and you may find that the statutory agencies are sometimes hungry for your views about how services should be developed. You may even be asked to join a focus group.

Change happens slowly, and the process is frustrating, with similar questions being asked over and over, and findings and reports being set out in glossy booklets that often state the obvious but don't seem to lead anywhere. But things are improving. When you enter the Family Business and the disability world, it is essential to stay upbeat, to speak up for your child and to retain your sense of humour. As the Monty Python song goes: 'Always look on the bright side of life!'

The other day, while we were eating our tea, the subject of "how lucky we are" came up in conversation. I can't remember what triggered it; I think there had been a report on the news about a natural disaster in a far-off place, with images of misery, grief and poverty.

'Yes, we're so lucky to live where we do and have everything we need,' said Evie.

'So try and finish the last couple of mouthfuls of dinner, William,' I said. 'Think of those poor children who don't have enough to eat.' I knew immediately that was a silly thing to say, and of course William retorted:

'Why don't we send it to them, then? Anyway, it tastes a bit burnt to me,' he added mischievously, glancing at Evie.

I pushed a forkful of pasta between his lips, which parted as it approached, like a baby sparrow's beak, and he chomped away for a few moments. Then he said, 'I think I am really lucky.'

'That's good, William,' said Evie. 'Why do you think that?'

He scooped up the remains of his dinner, put it into his mouth by himself, and began chewing, taking his time, keeping us in suspense.

Would he tell us that he was lucky because he had nice parents, maybe? Or because he had such lovely brothers and a sister? Or because he was part of a happy family?

The answer, when it came at last, didn't feature any of these things. 'I'm lucky because I'm so cool,' he said.

Having finished tea, William trundled into the living room. He's just discovered the doubtful delights of *YouTube* and wanted to look at the latest McFly video and join in with the singing. He paused for a quick look at himself in the hall mirror on the way.

Afterwards, when we thought about it, Evie and I agreed that it was the best answer William could have given. Despite all he has to put up with in life, he feels he's "cool". He has a sense of feeling good about himself and secure about his place in the world. What more could parents wish for?

Reproduced from *The Family Business*, by Robert Marsden, published by BAAF in 2008 (pp 129–142).
© Robert Marsden

Buy a good aluminium stepladder: some tips from a single parent

I've now been a single parent for quite some time and, as an "old" hand (not so much of the "old", thank you!), I've been asked to talk to other women – and men – who are thinking about adoption and want to know what it's "really like" to adopt without a partner. It's a difficult question to answer because, as I know from my own experience, it's hard to hear and understand what life will be like as a single parent of an adopted child until you're there.

Besides, you don't want to put people off by being too brutally frank; and all children are different, as are all parents. But just in case it's helpful and hoping I won't frighten anyone away, here are my top tips:

Think carefully about why you want to become a parent; adoption is about what's best for the child, not what's convenient for you. Children who have to be separated from their birth families are not meant to fill a gap in our lives.

Never apologise for being a single parent. Look for an agency that welcomes single people and has experience of placing children in one-parent families. You should never feel that they would have preferred you to be one of a couple. Don't be afraid to ask them to put you in touch with other single adopters, for example. If you're comfortable with being single, then your child will be comfortable with it too.

Be prepared for your life to change radically. Don't think you'll be able to simply slip an adopted child into your life and carry on as normal. Talk to as many single adopters as you can, but also to one-parent birth families. There may be differences in your family circumstances, but they will understand many of the challenges that you will face and where to go to get help.

Sort out your financial situation before you commit yourself. Nothing is cheaper for two than for one, especially if one of you breaks and loses things, tears clothes and grows larger at an alarming rate! You don't need to be rich to be a single parent, but you do need to be able to maintain a comfortable lifestyle. Think hard about whether or not you'll be able to carry on working and, if you can't carry on with your job, carefully think through how you're going to earn money to support your new family. There is a single parent adviser at my local Job Centre. Check out yours!

Build up a network of support among friends, relations and neighbours. Keep them interested and involved. I can't tell you how important this is. Sometimes it's hard to ask for help, even from those closest to you, so make sure the people you rely on are ready to support you in a crisis. You don't have anything to prove, so don't be afraid to admit you need help. We all do – well, I do, that's for sure! For your own peace of mind, agree with your relatives who will look after your adopted child if the worst should happen to you – it's tricky, but essential, and it will make you feel better.

Grow a thicker skin and develop your laughter muscles! The best way to deal with other people's lack of tact and understanding is to have a good laugh about it. It's hard to be held responsible for your child's misdemeanours, harder still if you can't go home and let off steam to a partner, so phone a friend with a good sense of humour and poke fun at the situation. It'll help you put it all into perspective. The odd glass of wine helps, too!

Buy a good aluminium stepladder and a wheelbarrow! You will be surprised at how much more fixing, mending, decorating and lifting of heavy things has to be done once you're a family unit. And while you are at it, develop a special skill like putting up a large tent on your own or changing a wheel at the roadside – your child may even help, and onlookers will be full of admiration (or you could do what I did and use your Tesco Clubcard vouchers to join the RAC. I think that was extremely resourceful of me!).

Keep a life of your own. This is easier said than done and requires a lot of effort at times when you'd just like to collapse in a heap in front of the telly. But it's worth it, because children don't stay in the nest forever, and you will have a lot of living to do after they leave home. Don't be afraid of giving your wholehearted attention to a child who needs the security and stability of a loving family, but remember that you won't be able to be a good parent, with a proper sense of perspective, if your whole life revolves around your child. You'll also be very boring and won't be invited to parties!

Don't rush into anything. Always have a plan, and always have a plan B. So, whether you're going shopping, drawing money out of the bank, planning a trip, or a day out, or simply spending the day at home with your child, be proactive. In my experience, every time I just "let things happen" things seem to go wrong. So, even though it's a drag at times, think ahead about what you're doing. It'll help you relax and enjoy life, honest!

No one is going to tell you that adopting on your own is easy – because it isn't. Is it worth it, though? Yes, most definitely. I have a happy and loving little boy to share my life with. It's like having sunshine every day! So if you're considering adopting on your own and, after reading all this you still feel you can do it, my advice is 'Go for it'. You won't regret it.

Reproduced from *Flying Solo*, by Julia Wise, published by BAAF in 2007 (pp 124–127). © Julia Wise

Keep an eye on the prize!

All families have to deal with challenging behaviour. It is difficult to know if it is because of the children's past or if it is just natural for their age. For example, Ryan can be mean to Carly – now is this sibling rivalry, to do with their history, or something else happening at school? Historically, Ryan was favoured and Carly almost starved to death, so obviously, that could be the explanation.

I had to restrain Ryan once because he was kicking and screaming. He gets a look in his eye and just stares at you. It seems to happen every three months. It may be linked to stuff going on at school. Ryan is not very academic because he missed out on school before he moved in with us.

Ryan has loads of energy so you have to find ways of getting rid of that. It is harder when it rains. For example, one day in half-term, we had done loads of stuff but by eight in the evening, we all needed time out away from each other. Sometimes, they can drive me mental. Other times they can be very loving and adorable. Ryan writes little notes saying, 'I love my mums'.

For the first nine months, Carly loved Sophie when she came home from work but hated me, who was the one looking after her at home and, of course, having to tell her off sometimes.

One day, I trapped her finger in the front door, by mistake. We were in a rush to a Hallowe'en party, so she was in fancy dress. We rushed to an NHS walk-in centre but luckily, nothing was broken. When we came home, she sat on my knee and cried and I rocked her. I felt terrible but actually that episode changed things. She realised that I was there for her and was going to look after her. I put on a film and soothed her and we sat there for a couple of hours – just the two of us. There was a look in her eye that day and I knew something had clicked.

They both love living here now. I was brought up in quite impoverished circumstances and I look at them and think they are a lot better off.

We are constantly reassuring them that this is their family. Our password is 'I love you'. We've forgotten almost that they are adopted.

What impact has adoption had on your life?

Life was fantastic before, we both had well-paid jobs, we would go to Florence for a weekend, etc, but it always felt as if something was missing. I remember during the two weeks of introductions, sitting in a family restaurant that we would never have gone to before. I looked over at a young couple without children and thought – you are free. I did have a yearning for our old life then.

In the first few months we used to argue over who would pop out to get milk just to get some time on our own and feel free to stare into space.

Luckily, Sophie and I have a lovely relationship and we support each other. However, we have had to make sacrifices and are nowhere near as frisky as we used to be. We can't just do as we please any more.

Our house used to be like a pristine show home but now we have fingerprints on our Farrow and Ball walls and book bags, tennis rackets and stickers everywhere. The garden is ruined from Ryan playing football.

Holidays now cost a fortune. We went on a five-star holiday to India before the children, while last year we spent the same money on a two-week caravan holiday in the UK.

I used to run a nightclub and have spiky hair and now I'm organising parent/teacher events and seem very respectable – I can see the funny side of it!

What have you learned about yourself?

I have learned a lot about being a mum. It has opened my eyes to many things and introduced me to a new way of looking at things happening in society, for example, anti-social behaviour – now I might try to understand why it is happening. I realise now how important it is to feel secure. If children's needs are not met, they are going to feel angry.

How do you feel about not being a birth mother?

It doesn't bother me. I never felt the need to give birth. Actually, I feel very proud of the fact that we have adopted, especially as a same-sex couple. I think it is actually easier, as a same-sex couple, to say that you have adopted children rather than giving birth to them, but I hope, in time, that attitudes will change.

In terms of my love for the children, I feel I could stop a train coming towards them with my own body. I don't think I could love a birth child any more than I love them.

What would you say to someone thinking of adopting?

It is the best thing I have ever done and gives me a lot of pleasure. However, you really need to think about it, ask yourself about your motivation and your approach to bringing up children. Don't be defensive with social workers and remain open-minded. I think your approach determines how people react to you. Be patient with social workers, sometimes they have to get four or five colleagues around a table to make a decision.

Be excited about what you are doing and keep an eye on the prize; for us it was not only doing a good deed but building a family.

Reproduced from *Proud Parents*, by Nicola Hill, published by BAAF in 2013 (pp 143–146). © Nicola Hill

A poem for my mum

George (at age 20)

My sky changed from black to blue

The day I came to live with you,

I was lost, like moving sand

No more, because I am found,

From day one you treated me like your own son

I am proud to call you mum

(p 109)

Every child is special

Julia (at age 14)

I was adopted when I was small. I lived with a foster family for a short while. I have contact with my eldest sister by letter. She sounds so lovely and when I am older I may meet her. I have more birth sisters but have no contact with them. I would like to though. I am the youngest child in my birth family, but the eldest in the family I have now...my forever family.

I love playing sport and being with my friends who I love and miss a lot when I am away from school. I love my school and my family and I have amazing friends, some of which are older than me. All my friends are so lovely and sometimes when things are not so great I talk to them. Obviously everyone feels sad in their lives, even a non-adopted person, and it's really important you can talk to someone you trust about how you feel.

I am glad I am adopted, although adoption brings with it feelings of loss, sadness, anger and many, many more feelings it also brings great joy and happiness to everyone involved. My parents were given a chance to have a child they otherwise couldn't have, my biological parents tried to rebuild their lives and I was given a second chance to have a happier life. I would like to say thank you to my family for adopting me and for being the best ever. I love them so much. They have changed my life so much for the better, I could never describe how much.

When I am older, maybe when I am a granny, after I have been a policewoman and a mummy and a sailing instructor for disabled children, I would like to be a foster mum and be able to give other children another chance in life like I was given. I think it is a lovely thing to do as children also have feelings which are valid and should be recognised and every child deserves to be loved no matter who they are or what they are like. Every child is special and worth something in the world.

(p 106)

Reproduced from *The Colours in Me*, edited by Perlita Harris, published by BAAF in 2008. © BAAF

What I am looking forward to

....

....

....

....

....

....

....

....

....

....

....

....

....

....

....

....

....

....

....

....

....

....

....

....

References

BAAF (2013) *The Prospective Adopter's Report* (England), London: BAAF

Ainsworth MDS, Bell S and Stayton D (1971) 'Individual differences in strange-situation behaviour of one-year-olds', in Schaffer H (ed) *The Origins of Human Social Relations*, New York, NY: Academic Press, pp. 17–52

American Psychiatric Association (1994) *Diagnostic and Statistical Manual of the American Psychiatric Association*, New York, NY: American Psychiatric Association

Archer C (1999) *Parenting the Child Who Hurts: First steps – tiddlers and toddlers*, London: Jessica Kingsley Publishers

Archer C (1999) *Parenting the Child Who Hurts: Next steps – tykes and teens*, London: Jessica Kingsley Publishers

Argent H (ed) (1995) *See You Soon: Contact with children looked after by local authorities*, London: BAAF

Argent H and Coleman J (2006) *Dealing with Disruption*, London: BAAF

Bateson G (2000) *Steps to an Ecology of Mind*, Chicago, IL: University of Chicago Press

Beek M and Schofield G (2004) *Providing a Secure Base in Long-Term Foster Care*, London: BAAF

Beesley P (2015) *Making Good Assessments: A practical resource guide*, London: CoramBAAF

Bowlby J (1988) *A Secure Base: Clinical applications of attachment theory*, London: Routledge

Braithwaite J (1989) *Crime, Shame and Reintegration*, Cambridge: Cambridge University Press

Bronfenbrenner U (1979) *The Ecology of Human Development: Experiments by nature and design*, Cambridge, MA: Harvard University Press

Cairns B (2004) *Fostering Attachments*, London: BAAF

Cairns K and Fursland E (2007) *Trauma and Recovery*, London: BAAF

Cooper C (1985) '"Good enough" borderline and "bad enough" parenting', in Adcock M and White R (eds) *Good Enough Parenting*, London: BAAF

Cousins J (2003) 'Are we missing the match? Rethinking adopter assessment and child profiling', *Adoption & Fostering*, 27:4, pp. 7–18

Crittenden PM (1995) 'Attachment and psychopathology', in Goldberg S, Muir R and Kerr J (eds) *Attachment Theory: Social, developmental and clinical perspectives*, Hillsdale, NJ: Analytical Press, pp. 367–406

Dance C and Rushton A (2005) 'Predictors of outcome for unrelated adoptive placements made during middle childhood', *Child & Family Social Work*, 10, pp. 269–280

Dance C, Ouwejan D, Beecham J and Farmer E (2010) *Linking and Matching: A survey of adoption agency practice in England and Wales*, London: BAAF

Demos V (ed) (1995) *Exploring Affect: The selected writings of Silvan S Tomkins*, Cambridge: Cambridge University Press

Department for Children, Schools and Families (2003) *Every Child Matters*, London: DCSF

Department for Children, Schools and Families (2010) *Working Together to Safeguard Children*, London: DCSF

Department for Education (2012) *Government's Action Plan for Adoption: Tackling delay*, London: The Stationery Office

Department for Education (2013) *Adoption Agencies (Miscellaneous Amendments) Regulations 2013* para 24 (2a–2f), London: The Stationery Office

Department of Health (2000) *Framework for the Assessment of Children in Need and their Families*, London: The Stationery Office

Dozier M, Lindheim O, Lewis E, Bick, Bernard K and Peloso E (2009) 'Effects of a foster parent training program on young children's attachment behaviours: Preliminary evidence from a randomised clinical trial', *Child and Adolescent Social Work*, 26, pp. 321–332

Fahlberg V (1994) *A Child's Journey through Placement*, London: BAAF

Glaser D and Prior V (1997) 'Is the term child protection applicable to emotional abuse?', *Child Abuse Review*, 6:5, pp. 315-329

Glaser D (2000) 'Child abuse and neglect and the brain: a review', *Journal of Child Psychology & Psychiatry*, 41:1, pp 97–116

Horwath J (2007) *Child Neglect: Identification and assessment*, Basingstoke: Palgrave Macmillan

Howe D (2011) *Attachment across the Life Course: A brief introduction*, Basingstoke: Macmillan

Howe D, Brandon M, Hinings D and Schofield G (1999) *Attachment Theory, Child Maltreatment and Family Support: A practice and assessment model*, Basingstoke: Macmillan

Hughes D (1997) *Facilitating Developmental Attachment: The road to emotional recovery and behavioural change in foster and adoptive children*, New York, NY: Jason Aronson Inc

Hughes D (1998) *Building the Bonds of Attachment: Awakening love in deeply troubled children*, New York, NY: Jason Aronson

Jowitt S (2003) *Child Neglect: Contemporary themes and issues: policy and practice in child welfare*, Literature Review series 2, Glasbury-on-Wye: Bridge Publishing House

Kaufman G (1992) *Shame: The power of caring*, Rochester, VT: Schenkman Books

Kohnstamm R (2002) *Kleine ontwikkelingspsychologie I*, Houten/Diegem: Bohn Stafleu Van Loghum

Lord J and Cullen D (2013) *Effective Adoption Panels*, 6th edition, London: BAAF

Main M and Solomon J (1986) 'Discovery of an insecure/disorganised/disoriented attachment pattern', in Braselton TB and Yogwan MW (eds) *Affective Development in Infancy*, Norwood, NJ:

Ablex, pp. 95–124

Main M and Hesse E (1990) 'Parents' unresolved traumatic experiences are related to infant disorganised attachment status: is frightened and/or frightening the linking mechanism?', in Greenberg MT and Cummings EM (eds) *Attachment in the Preschool Years: Theory, research and intervention*, Chicago, IL: University of Chicago Press, pp. 161–182

Meins E, Fermyhough C, Wainwright R, Clark-Carter D, Das Gupta M, Fradley E, and Tuckey M (2003) 'Pathways to understanding mind: construct of maternal validity and predictive validity of natural mind-mindedness' *Child Development*, 14;4 pp. 637–648

Neil E and Howe D (2004) *Contact in Adoption and Permanent Foster Care: Research, theory and practice*, London: BAAF

NICE (2009) *When to Suspect Child Maltreatment*, Clinical Guidelines 89, London: NICE

Perry B (1999) *Effects of Traumatic Events on Children: Interdisciplinary education series*, Volume 2, Number 3, Houston, TX: Child Trauma Academy

Perry BD (2002) 'Childhood experience and the expression of genetic potential: what childhood neglect tells us about nature and nurture', *Brain and Mind*, 3, pp. 79–100

Quinton D, Rushton A, Dance C and Mayes D (1998) *Joining New Families: A study of adoption and fostering in middle childhood*, Chichester: John Wiley

Russell J (2006) 'Fostering and adoption disruption research: secondary analysis' available at: www.jameslyonrussell.com/fosteringandadoptiondisruptions.pdf

Schofield G and Beek M (2009) 'Growing up in foster care: providing a secure base through adolescence', *Child and Family Social Work*, 14:3, pp. 255–266

Spencer N and Baldwin N (2005) 'Economic, cultural and social contexts of neglect', in Taylor D and Daniel B (eds) *Child Neglect: Practice issues for health and social care*, London: Jessica Kingsley Publishers, pp. 26–42

Stevenson O (2007) *Neglected Children and their Families*, Oxford: Blackwell

Taylor J and Daniel B (2005) *Child Neglect: Practice issues for health and social care*, London: Jessica Kingsley Publishers

Teicher M (14 Dec 2000) www.researchmatters.harvard.edu

Wilson K, Sinclair I and Petrie S (2003) 'A kind of loving: a model of effective foster care', *British Journal of Social Work*, 33, pp. 991–1003

Triseliotis J, Shireman J and Hundelby M (1997) *Adoption: Theory, policy and practice*, London: Cassell

Suggested reading

Most of the books listed here can be purchased from CoramBAAF. Visit our bookshop at www.corambaaf.org.uk/bookshop, or contact Publications Sales on 020 7520 7517, or at pubs.sales@corambaaf.org.uk.

BOOKS TO READ DURING STAGE 1

Harris P (ed) (2008) *The Colours in Me*, London: BAAF
A unique collection of poetry, prose and artwork by adopted children and young people.

Hill N (2012) *The Pink Guide to Adoption for Lesbians and Gay Men*, London: BAAF
A step-by-step guide to adoption which explores how being a prospective gay or lesbian adopter can affect this.

Lilley J (2016) *Our Adoption Journey*, London: CoramBAAF
The true story of an adoption, following Jayne's and Dan's journey to adopting a baby girl.

Lord J (2016) *Adopting a Child*, London: BAAF
The definitive guide to adopting a child, with information about the kinds of children who need adopting, the process, and contact details for adoption agencies.

Wise J (2007) *Flying Solo*, London: BAAF
This humorous account describes the realities of the author's life as a single adopter with a young boy.

CoramBAAF's Advice Note series includes a number of short booklets which provide basic information on adoption issues. Titles include: *Adoption: Some questions answered, The Preparation and Assessment Process (Adoption), Contact: If you are adopting a child*, and *Children's Special Needs: Some questions answered.*

BOOKS TO READ DURING STAGE 2, BEFORE GOING TO PANEL

May P (2005) *Approaching Fatherhood: A guide for adoptive dads and others*, London: BAAF
The first book in the UK to look at the adoption process – from the father's point of view.

Argent H (2014) *Related by Adoption*, London: BAAF
This book gives grandparents-to-be and other relatives information about adoption today and how it will affect them.

Personal narratives by adopters

Ashton L (2008) *Take Two*, London: BAAF
Examines the emotional and physical demands of IVF, and the family's eventual decision to adopt two baby girls.

Belle J (2010) *When Daisy met Tommy*, London: BAAF
The story of how six-year-old birth child Daisy and her parents adopt baby Tom.

Butcher M (2010) *Frozen*, London: BAAF
Written from the perspective of the adoptive father, this honest account documents IVF treatment going wrong and how adoption finally changes the couple's life.

Carr K (2007) *Adoption Undone*, London: BAAF
The story of an adoption breakdown, bravely told by the adoptive mother.

Clay R (2011) *Is it True you have Two Mums?*, London: BAAF
The story of a dual-heritage lesbian couple who adopt three daughters.

Fernández P (2011) *Becoming Dads*, London: BAAF
The story of a gay couple and their journey through the adoption process to becoming dads to a young boy.

Harris P (ed) (2006) *In Search of Belonging: Reflections by transracially adopted people*, London: BAAF
An anthology of writings and artwork from over 50 transracial and transnational UK adopted people.

Hirst M (2005) *Loving and Living with Traumatised Children: Reflections by adoptive parents*, London: BAAF
An account of the experiences of nine individuals who adopted traumatised children.

Mackenzie G and Mackenzie J (2011) *As if I was a Real Boy*, London: BAAF
The story of how Gordon, who was 10 and living in a psychiatric hospital with undiagnosed mental health issues, was adopted by Jeannie.

Marsden R (2008) *The Family Business*, London: BAAF
A revealing story of the adoption of William, a little boy with cerebral palsy, by a middle-aged couple with three birth children.

Massiah H (ed) (2005) *Looking after our Own: The stories of black and Asian adopters*, London: BAAF
A collection of the experiences of nine adopters and their families.

Royce R and Royce E (2008) *Together in Time*, London: BAAF
A couple look back on their experiences of adopting two boys with attachment difficulties, and how art and music therapy helped their family.

BOOKS TO READ WHILE WAITING TO BE MATCHED WITH A CHILD

Fahlberg V (1995) *A Child's Journey through Placement*, London: CoramBAAF
This essential reference text contains the theoretical knowledge base and skills necessary for understanding children who have suffered separation, loss and grief.

Cairns K and Cairns B (2016) *Attachment, Trauma and Resilience: Therapeutic caring for children*, London: CoramBAAF
A heartwarming and insightful book based on the authors' own experiences of permanent fostering, which looks at strategies families can use to help traumatised children.

Salter A (2012) *The Adopter's Handbook*, London: BAAF
A "must-have" guide to help families help themselves throughout the adoption process and afterwards.

Gerhardt S (2014) *Why Love Matters: How affection shapes a baby's brain,* Hove and New York, Brunner-Routledge
An accessible interpretation of the latest findings in neuroscience about how the human brain is shaped by experiences in the early years.

Parenting Matters series

This CoramBAAF series offers a sound introduction to a range of health conditions common in looked after children and offer a glimpse of what it might be like to live with an affected child.

Parenting a Child with Attention Deficit Hyperactivity Disorder, Brian Jacobs and Lorna Miles, 2012

Parenting a Child with Dyslexia, Chris Stanway and Lorna Miles, 2012

Parenting a Child with Mental Health Issues, Catherine Jackson, 2012

Parenting a Child Affected by Parental Substance Misuse, Donald Forrester, 2012

Parenting a Child with Emotional and Behavioural Difficulties, Dan Hughes, 2012

Parenting a Child with Autism Spectrum Disorder, Paul Carter, 2013

Parenting a Child with Developmental Delay, Pamela Bartram and Sue and Jim Clifford, 2013

Parenting a Child with, or at Risk of, Genetic Disorders, Peter Turnpenny, 2013

Parenting a Child affected by Domestic Violence, Hedy Cleaver, 2015

Parenting a Child affected by Sexual Abuse, Biddy Youell, 2016

Parenting a Child who has experienced Trauma, Dan Hughes, 2016

BOOKS TO READ DURING INTRODUCTIONS AND THE EARLY DAYS OF ADOPTION

Verrier N (2009) *The Primal Wound: Understanding the adopted child,* London: CoramBAAF
A classic adoption text which has revolutionised the way we think about adoption, with its exploration of the "primal wound" that results when a child is separated from his or her mother.

Archer C (1999) *First Steps in Parenting the Child who Hurts,* London: Jessica Kingsley Publishers
This book offers practical, sensitive guidance through the areas of separation, loss and trauma in early childhood.

Archer C (1999) *Next Steps in Parenting the Child who Hurts,* London: Jessica Kingsley Publishers
Following on from First Steps, this book continues the journey through late childhood and into adolescence, explaining the effects of early emotional trauma.

BOOKS TO READ LATER ON

Morrison M (2012) *Talking about Adoption to your Adopted Child*, London: BAAF
This comprehensive guide outlines the whys, whens and hows of telling the truth about an adopted child's origins.

Wolfs R (2008) *Adoption Conversations: What, when and how to tell*, London: BAAF
An in-depth practical guide which explores the questions adopted children are likely to ask.

Fursland E (2010) *Facing up to Facebook: A survival guide for adoptive families*, London: BAAF
This practical guide explores the issues raised by social networking websites for adoptive families.

Gilligan R (2009) *Promoting Resilience*, London: BAAF
This book explores the concept of resilience, and includes many practical ideas for how to promote this in children.

Lacher D B, Nichols T and May J (2005) *Connecting with Kids through Stories: Using narratives to facilitate attachment in adopted children*, London: Jessica Kingsley Publishers
This practical book looks at how to use storytelling to aid therapeutic work with troubled children.

Ryan T and Walker R (2016) *Life Story Work*, London: BAAF
This book explores and explains the concept of life story work, and includes an assortment of creative techniques and exercises.

Stringer B (2009) *Communicating through Play*, London: BAAF
This guide offers a variety of techniques for helping adults to engage with children and enhance relationship through the medium of play.

BOOKS TO USE WITH CHILDREN

Argent H (2007) *Josh and Jaz have Three Mums*, London: BAAF
This story helps to explain the diversity and "difference" of family groups, and encourages an understanding and appreciation of same-sex parents.

Bagnall S (2008) *The Teazles' Baby Bunny*, London: BAAF
This simple book for young children provides a gentle introduction to broaching the subject of adoption.

Bell M (2008) *Elfa and the Box of Memories*, London: BAAF
This story looks at the importance of memories, both good and bad, and how they help us to remember the story of our lives.

Edwards B (2010) *The Most Precious Present in the World*, London: BAAF
This story looks at themes of loss, separation and belonging, and explains that it is alright to have mixed feelings about adoption.

Foxon J (2003) *Nutmeg gets Adopted*, London: BAAF

The first title in the six-book Nutmeg series, which follows Nutmeg the squirrel's adoption journey.

Griffiths J (2007) *Picnic in the Park*, London: BAAF
This colourful book introduces young children to varied contemporary family structures.

Merchant E (2010) *Dad David, Baba Chris and Me*, London: BAAF
This story helps to explain the diversity and "difference" of family groups, and encourages an understanding and appreciation of same-sex parents.

Pitcher D (2008) *Where is Poppy's Panda?*, London: BAAF
This story explores transition, loss, change and the importance of maintaining continuity in a child's life.

Seeney J (2007) *Morris and the Bundle of Worries*, London: BAAF
This story explores the importance of sharing worries and thereby learning to cope and manage them.